It's Another Ace Book from CGP

This book is for anyone doing OCR Science — Staged Assessment.

We've stuck in all the _really important stuff_ you need
to do well in your OCR Year 10 Science Exam.

Then we had a real good stab at trying
to make it funny — so you'll _actually use it_.
Simple as that.

> **Higher**
> Some of the material is only needed at Higher level.
> We've stuck this stuff in blue boxes (like this one) so it's easy to find in the book.

> **Year 11 Exam**
> Anything in a red box (like this one) is stuff that could be in
> both the Year 10 and Year 11 Exams.
> So don't throw this book away after Year 10. You'll be needing it again.

CGP are just the best

The central aim of Coordination Group Publications is to produce
top quality books that are carefully written, immaculately
presented and marvellously funny — whilst always making sure they
exactly cover the National Curriculum for each subject.

And then we supply them to as many people as we possibly can,
as _cheaply_ as we possibly can.

Buy our books — they're ace

Year 10 Revision Guide — Contents

Module BD1 — Supplying the Cell

Module BD2 — Control in Animals and Plants

Module BD3 — Ecology

Module CD1 — Equations and Rates of Reaction

Year 10 Revision Guide

Contents

Published by: Coordination Group Publications Ltd
Illustrations by: Sandy Gardner e-mail: zimkit@aol.com
and Bowser, Colorado USA

Updated by: Matthew Ball
Chris Bates MMath (Hons) GIMA
Gemma Hallam MA Hons. (Cantab)
Tim Major
Tessa Moulton BSc (Hons)
Andy Park BSc (Hons)
Philip Robson
Julie Schofield

ISBN 1-84146-950-5
Groovy Website: www.cgpbooks.co.uk

Printed by Elanders Hindson, Newcastle upon Tyne.
Clipart sources: CorelDRAW and VECTOR.

Proofreading by:
Alison Odds

Cells

Plant Cells and Animal Cells Have Their Differences

You need to be able to draw these two cells with all the details for each.

Animal Cell

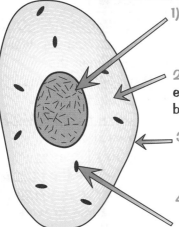

Plant Cell

FOUR THINGS THEY BOTH HAVE IN COMMON:

1) **NUCLEUS** contains genetic material that controls what the cell does.

2) **CYTOPLASM** contains enzymes that speed up biological reactions.

3) **CELL MEMBRANE** holds the cell together and controls what goes in and out.

4) **MITOCHONDRIA** turn glucose and oxygen into energy.

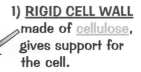

THREE EXTRAS THAT ONLY THE PLANT CELL HAS:

1) **RIGID CELL WALL** made of cellulose, gives support for the cell.

2) **VACUOLE** contains cell sap, a weak solution of sugar and salts.

3) **CHLOROPLASTS** containing chlorophyll for photosynthesis. *Found in the green parts of plants.*

Cells are Specialised for their Function

Most cells are specialised for a specific job, and in the Exam you'll probably have to explain why the cell they've shown you is so good at its job. It's a lot easier if you've already learnt them!

1) Red blood cells are Designed to Carry Oxygen

1) They're small and doughnut shaped to give a big surface area for oxygen absorption.
2) They contain haemoglobin which carries oxygen.
3) They're flexible to allow smooth passage through the capillaries.
4) They're unusual because they don't need a nucleus.

2) White blood cells are made to Fight Disease

White blood cells have a flexible shape.
This allows them to engulf disease organisms.

3) Leaf palisade cells contain many Chloroplasts

1) The large number of chloroplasts means they contain loads of chlorophyll — just what's needed for photosynthesis.
2) Leaf palisade cells are tall — which means there's a good chance of light hitting a chloroplast before reaching the bottom of the cell.

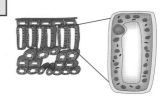

Have you learnt it? — let's see, shall we...

Right then, when you're ready, when you think you've learnt it, cover the page and answer these:
1) Draw an animal cell and a plant cell and put all the labels on them.
2) What four things do plant and animal cells have in common?
3) What are the three differences between them?
4) Name two specialised human cells. What are their special features?

The Digestive System

You'll definitely get a question on this in your Exam so take your time and learn this very important diagram in all its infinite glory. And that includes the words too:

Eight Bits of Your Grisly Digestive System to Learn:

(...plus the tongue)

Tongue

Stomach

1) It PUMMELS THE FOOD with its muscular walls.
2) It produces the PROTEASE enzyme.
3) It produces HYDROCHLORIC ACID for two reasons:
   a) to kill bacteria
   b) to give the right pH for the protease enzyme to work (pH2 - acidic).

Oesophagus

— ie, the gullet. This is the 'food chute' from the mouth to the stomach.

Liver

Where BILE is produced. Bile EMULSIFIES FATS and neutralises stomach acid (to make conditions right for the enzymes in the small intestine).

Pancreas

Produces all three enzymes: PROTEASE, CARBOHYDRASE and LIPASE.

Gall bladder

Where bile is stored before being injected into the intestine via the BILE DUCT.

Small intestine

1) Produces all the three enzymes: PROTEASE, CARBOHYDRASE and LIPASE.
2) This is also where the "food" is absorbed into the blood.
3) The inner surface is covered with villi to increase the surface area. It's also very long.

Large intestine

Where excess water is absorbed from the food.

Rectum

Where the faeces are stored before they bid you a fond farewell through the anus.

Have you learned the whole diagram...

The one thing they won't ask you to do in the Exam is draw the whole thing out yourself. BUT they will ask you about any part of it, eg. "What is the position of the liver?", or "What does the pancreas produce?", or "What is the function of bile?" So in the end you have to learn the whole thing anyway. And that means being able to cover the page and draw it out, words and all. If you can't draw it all out from memory — then you haven't learnt it. Simple as that.

Diffusion of "Food" Molecules

The Big Food Molecules Must First be Broken Down

Chewing your food up is the first stage of physical digestion ('physical' just means there's no chemicals involved). After that it's your stomach's turn to try and munch it up still further. The stomach gives the food a good pummelling — and it produces protease enzymes, which break down proteins. On top of all this, the stomach produces acid, which helps the enzymes to work properly.

Even after the stomach's done its job, the food is still made up of quite big molecules, namely: STARCH, PROTEINS and FATS. These are still TOO BIG to diffuse into the blood, and so they are broken down by enzymes in the small intestine into smaller molecules: GLUCOSE, AMINO ACIDS and FATTY ACIDS & GLYCEROL. This process is called chemical digestion.

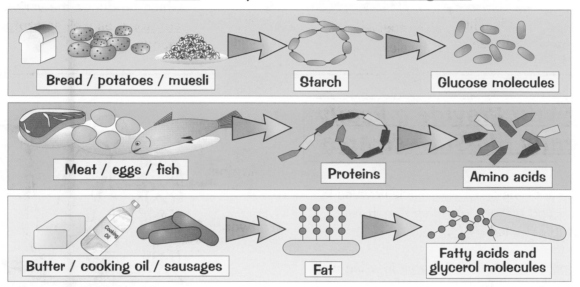

The Small Molecules Can Then Diffuse into the Blood

1) These molecules (glucose, amino acids, fatty acids and glycerol) are small enough to diffuse into the blood.

2) In fact, these molecules will only "diffuse" into the blood with the help of active transport (as used by plant root hairs) because the concentration gradient is the wrong way.

3) They then travel to where they're needed, and diffuse out again. It's all clever stuff.

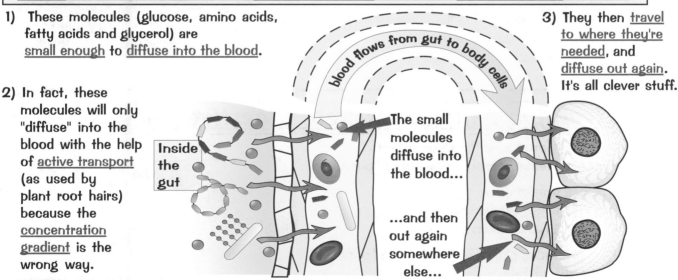

Let's see what you've LEARNED, shall we...

Practise answering these three questions until you can do them all without looking at the page. If you can't, then it means just one thing — you haven't learnt it. (Pretty obviously.)
1) Name the three big molecules that won't diffuse into the blood.
2) Name the four small molecules that will diffuse into the blood.
3) What is the name of the process that turns the big molecules into the small molecules?

Digestive System Extras

All the Way Along there's Muscular and Glandular Tissue

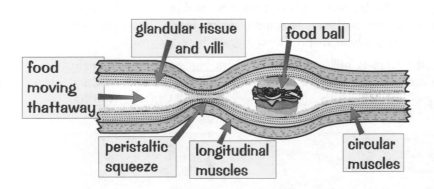

food moving thattaway

glandular tissue and villi

food ball

peristaltic squeeze

longitudinal muscles

circular muscles

There's muscular tissue all the way down the digestive system. Its job is to squeeze the food along. This squeezing action is called PERISTALSIS.

The inside layer is glandular tissue which produces the various enzymes, as well as protective mucus.

The Villi Provide a Really Really Big Surface Area

The inside of the small intestine is covered in millions and millions of these tiny little projections called VILLI.

They increase the surface area in a big way so that digested food is absorbed much more quickly into the blood.
Notice they have
    1) a very thin layer of cells,
    2) a very good blood supply
       to assist quick absorption.

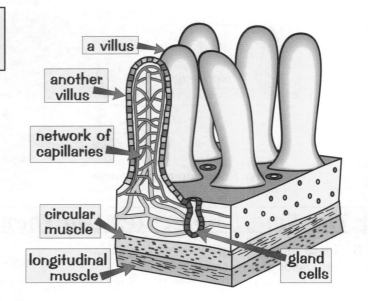

a villus

another villus

network of capillaries

circular muscle

longitudinal muscle

gland cells

The Liver and Pancreas Secrete Digestive Juices

1) The pancreas produces the three digestive enzymes protease, carbohydrase and lipase.

2) PROTEASE breaks down protein, CARBOHYDRASE breaks down carbohydrate and LIPASE breaks down fat.

3) The liver produces bile, which helps the lipase enzymes digest fats.

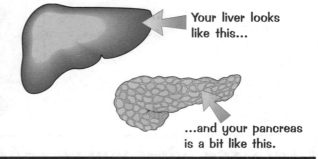

Your liver looks like this...

...and your pancreas is a bit like this.

So what have you LEARNED...

A real clever trick for learning lots of information is to get an overall image in your head of what each page looks like. It can really help you to remember all the little details. Try it with this page. Learn the two main diagrams, with all their little labels. Then cover the page and try and picture the whole thing in your head. Then try and scribble it all down. It takes practice but you can do it.

Enzymes

Enzymes seem to crop up in all sorts of places. That's cos they're great.

Enzymes **are** Biological Catalysts

1) <u>Living things</u> have thousands of different chemical processes going on inside them.

2) The <u>faster</u> these happen the <u>better</u>, and raising the <u>temperature</u> of the body is an important way to <u>speed them up</u>.

3) However, there's a <u>limit</u> to how far you can <u>raise</u> the temperature before <u>cells</u> start getting <u>damaged</u>, so living things also produce <u>enzymes</u> — these act as <u>catalysts</u> to <u>speed up</u> all these chemical reactions without the need for <u>high temperatures</u>.

4) A catalyst, remember, is just something that <u>speeds up</u> the rate of a reaction without being used up.

5) Every <u>different</u> biological process has its <u>own enzyme</u> designed especially for it.

Enzymes **Like it** Warm **but** Not Too Hot

1) The chemical reactions in <u>living cells</u> are quite fast in conditions that are <u>warm</u> rather than <u>hot</u>.

2) This is because the cells use <u>enzyme</u> catalysts, which are <u>protein molecules</u>.

3) Enzymes are usually <u>irreversibly damaged</u> (or <u>denatured</u>) by temperatures above about <u>45°C</u>, and as the graph shows, their activity drops off <u>sharply</u> when the temperature gets <u>a little too high</u>.

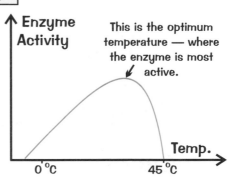

This is the optimum temperature — where the enzyme is most active.

Enzymes **Like the right** pH **too**

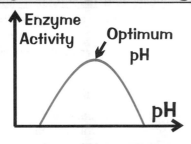

1) The <u>pH</u> affects the activity of enzymes, in a similar way to temperature.

2) The graph shows how the enzyme activity reaches a <u>peak</u> at a certain pH. If the pH is above or below this optimum level, the enzyme activity <u>falls</u>.

3) <u>Different</u> enzymes have <u>different</u> optimum pH levels.

BILE Neutralises the Stomach Acid and Emulsifies Fats

1) Bile is produced in the <u>LIVER</u>. It's <u>stored</u> in the <u>gall bladder</u> before it's released into the small intestine.

2) The hydrochloric acid in the stomach makes the pH <u>too acidic</u> for most enzymes to work properly. Bile is <u>alkaline</u> — it <u>neutralises</u> the acid and makes conditions alkaline. The enzymes in the small intestine <u>work best</u> in these <u>alkaline conditions</u>.

3) Bile also <u>emulsifies fats</u>. In other words it breaks the fat into <u>tiny droplets</u>. This gives a much <u>bigger surface area</u> of fat for the enzyme lipase to work on. Nothing too tricky there.

"Enzymes" — sounds like a brand of throat lozenge...

Enzymes are like my cat — they're pretty fussy about pretty much everything. Not only do they like the <u>temperature</u> to be just right — the <u>pH</u> has to be pretty much spot on as well. This page is definitely a candidate for the <u>mini-essay</u> method — close the book and write down everything you can remember about enzymes. Then look back to see what you've forgotten.

Lungs and Breathing

The Thorax

1) The thorax is the top part of your 'body' and is protected by the ribcage.

2) The lungs are like big pink sponges.

3) The trachea splits into two tubes called "bronchi" (each one is a "bronchus"), one going to each lung.

4) The bronchi split into progressively smaller tubes called bronchioles.

5) The bronchioles finally end at small bags called alveoli where the gas exchange takes place.

6) Bronchi and bronchioles both contain cartilage.

7) The cartilage is fairly rigid. It helps to keep the bronchi and bronchioles open if the pressure inside them drops.

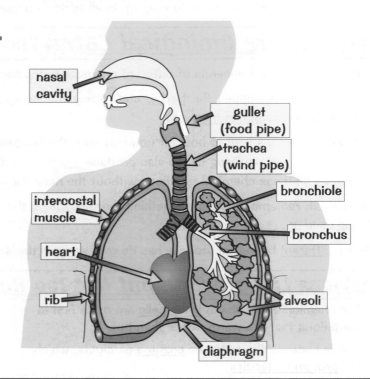

nasal cavity

gullet (food pipe)

trachea (wind pipe)

bronchiole

intercostal muscle

bronchus

heart

rib

alveoli

diaphragm

Ventilation

Moving air INTO and OUT OF the lungs is called VENTILATION.

Breathing In...

1) Intercostal muscles (ie. your rib muscles) and diaphragm contract.
2) Thorax volume increases, so the pressure decreases.
3) Air is drawn in due to decreased pressure.

...and Breathing Out

1) Intercostal muscles and diaphragm relax.
2) Thorax volume decreases, so the pressure increases.
3) Air is forced out due to increased pressure.

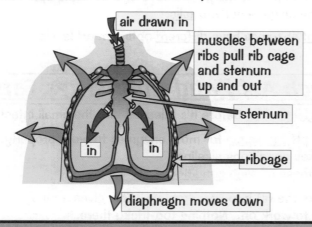

air drawn in

muscles between ribs pull rib cage and sternum up and out

sternum

ribcage

in   in

diaphragm moves down

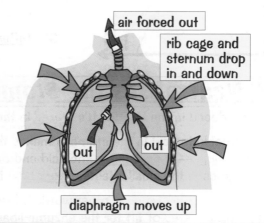

air forced out

rib cage and sternum drop in and down

out   out

diaphragm moves up

Stop huffing and puffing and just LEARN IT...

No dreary lists of facts this time anyway, just three splendid diagrams to learn. When you practise repeating diagrams from memory, you don't have to draw them really neatly, just sketch them clearly enough to label all the important bits. They'd never ask you to draw a really fancy diagram in the Exam, but they will expect you to label one. But the only way to be sure you really know a diagram is to sketch it and label it, all from memory.

Diffusion

Don't be put off by the fancy word

"Diffusion" is really simple. It's just the gradual net movement of particles from places where there are lots of them to places where there are fewer of them. That's all it is — it's just the natural tendency for stuff to spread out. Unfortunately you also have to learn the fancy way of saying the same thing, which is this:

DIFFUSION is the NET MOVEMENT OF PARTICLES from a region of HIGH CONCENTRATION to an area of LOW CONCENTRATION

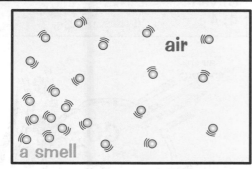

air

a smell

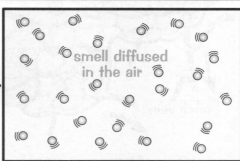

smell diffused in the air

Three Examples of Diffusion in the Body

1) Oxygen diffuses into the blood in the lungs...

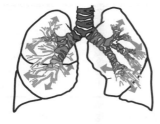

... and when the blood reaches the body tissues, it diffuses out.

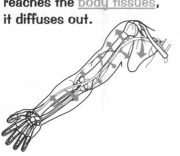

2) Carbon dioxide diffuses into the blood from the body tissues...

...and then diffuses out of the blood back in the lungs.

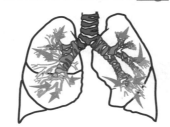

3) Food diffuses into the blood across the wall of the small intestine.

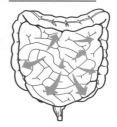

It then diffuses out of the blood and into various body tissues.

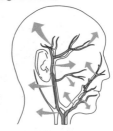

When food or gases are moving in and out of the blood, that's diffusion. Remember that.

So, how much do you know about diffusion?

Diffusion is common sense really. You'll be expected to mention diffusion if you get a question about gas transfer in the alveoli or food going into or out of the blood. Cover the page and write down the definition and the three examples of diffusion. Keep doing it until you get it right.

Alveoli and Gas Exchange

Alveoli are the tiny bags in the lungs where gas exchange takes place.

Alveoli

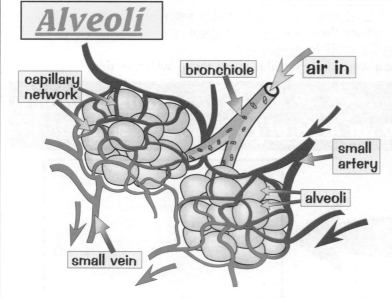

The alveoli are an ideal exchange surface. They have:

1) An enormous surface area (about 70m^2 in total).
2) A moist lining for dissolving gases.
3) Very thin walls.
4) A copious blood supply.

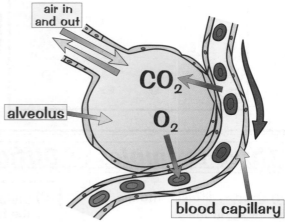

1) The job of the lungs is to transfer oxygen to the blood and to remove waste carbon dioxide from it.

2) To do this the lungs contain millions of alveoli where gas exchange takes place.

Gas Exchange at the Cells

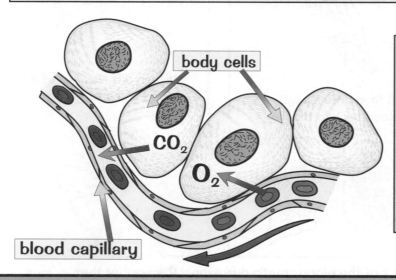

1) When the blood reaches the cells, oxygen is released from the oxyhaemoglobin in the red blood cells and diffuses into the body cells.

2) At the same time, carbon dioxide diffuses into the blood (plasma) to be carried back to the lungs.

This is a very easy page to learn...

Notice that the numbered points repeat information that the diagrams already show very clearly. The big idea is that you should understand and remember what goes on and why it all works so well. A clear visual image in your head of these diagrams makes it a lot easier. Learn the diagrams, words and all, until you can sketch them out entirely from memory.

The Circulatory System

The circulatory system's main function is to get food and oxygen to every cell in the body.
The diagram shows the basic layout, but make sure you learn the five important points too.

The DOUBLE Circulatory System, actually

The advantage of a double circulatory system is that it allows higher blood pressures.
This means there's a greater flow of blood round the body — and so all the cells get more oxygen.

①

The heart is actually two pumps.
The right side pumps deoxygenated blood to the lungs to collect oxygen.
Then the left side pumps this oxygenated blood around the body.

②

Arteries carry blood away from the heart at high pressure.

③

Normally, arteries carry oxygenated blood and veins carry deoxygenated blood.

④

The arteries eventually split off into thousands of tiny capillaries which take blood to every cell in the body.

⑤

The veins then collect the "used" blood and carry it back to the heart at low pressure to be pumped round again.

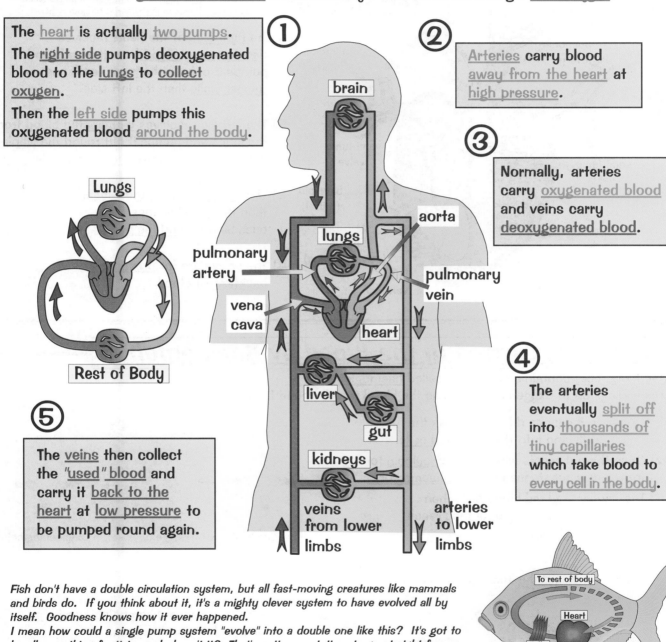

Lungs

Rest of Body

brain
aorta
lungs
pulmonary artery
pulmonary vein
vena cava
heart
liver
gut
kidneys
veins from lower limbs
arteries to lower limbs

To rest of body
Heart
Gills

Fish don't have a double circulation system, but all fast-moving creatures like mammals and birds do. If you think about it, it's a mighty clever system to have evolved all by itself. Goodness knows how it ever happened.
I mean how could a single pump system "evolve" into a double one like this? It's got to be all or nothing for it to work, hasn't it? That's quite a mutation, to go straight from a single pump heart that pumps to the lungs and then on to the rest of the body, to the double pump system shown above. But then life's full of little mysteries isn't it!

Let's see what you know then...

At least this stuff on the circulatory system is fairly interesting. Mind you, there are still plenty of picky little details you need to be clear about. And yes, you've guessed it, there's one sure-fire way to check just how clear you are — read it, learn it, then cover the page and reproduce it.
Having to sketch the diagram out again from memory is the only way to really learn it.

The Heart and Pumping Cycle

The heart is made almost entirely of <u>muscle</u>. And it's a <u>double pump</u>. Visualise the diagram with its <u>bigger side</u> full of <u>red, oxygenated blood</u>, and its <u>smaller side</u> full of <u>blue, deoxygenated blood</u>, and learn that the <u>left side</u> is <u>bigger</u>.

Learn **This** *Diagram* **of the** *Heart* **with** *All its* *Labels*

Right Side   *Left Side*

The left side of <u>your heart</u> is on <u>your left</u>. If you're facing someone, the left side of <u>their heart</u> is on <u>your right</u>.

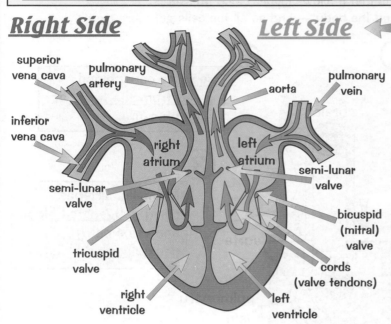

1) The <u>right side</u> of the heart receives <u>deoxygenated blood</u> from the body and pumps it only to the <u>lungs</u>, so it has <u>thinner walls</u> than the left side.

2) The <u>left side</u> receives <u>oxygenated blood</u> from the lungs and pumps it out round the <u>whole body</u>, so it has <u>thicker, more muscular walls</u>.

3) The <u>ventricles</u> are <u>much bigger</u> than the <u>atria</u> because they push blood <u>round the body</u>.

4) The <u>valves</u> are for <u>preventing backflow</u> of blood.

Oxygen **is Carried in the** *Blood* **by** *Haemoglobin*

<u>Red blood cells</u> contain a substance called <u>haemoglobin</u>, which clings on to oxygen molecules as the blood travels round the body.

1) Oxygen in the lungs <u>diffuses</u> across the <u>alveoli</u> walls and into the <u>red blood cells</u>.

2) Once there it reacts with the <u>haemoglobin</u> to form a new substance called <u>oxyhaemoglobin</u>.

3) The <u>oxygenated</u> red blood cells then travel around the body until they reach <u>various body tissues</u>.

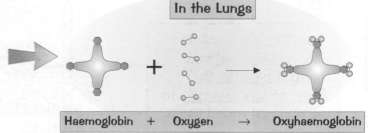

In the Lungs

Haemoglobin + Oxygen → Oxyhaemoglobin

In the Tissues

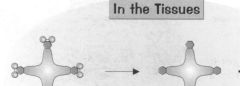

Oxyhaemoglobin → Haemoglobin + Oxygen

4) In the tissues the oxyhaemoglobin <u>splits up</u> into haemoglobin and oxygen.

5) The oxygen then <u>diffuses</u> out of the <u>red blood cells</u> into the <u>tissues</u>.

OK, let's get to the heart of the matter...

There's only one way to be <u>sure</u> you know all the details of the heart, and that's to learn the diagram until you can sketch it out, with all the labels, <u>from memory</u>. You need to know the <u>word equations</u> for the reaction of haemoglobin and oxygen, but they really aren't all that hard.

Blood Vessels

There are three different types of blood vessel and you need to know all about them:

Arteries Carry Blood Under Pressure

1) Arteries carry oxygenated blood away from the heart.
2) It comes out of the heart at high pressure, so the artery walls have to be strong and elastic.
3) Note how thick the walls are compared with the size of the hole down the middle (the "lumen" — silly name!).

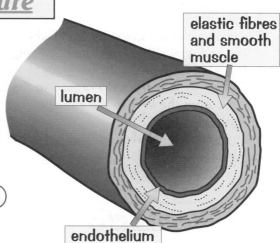

elastic fibres and smooth muscle

lumen

endothelium

Capillaries are Really Small

thin endothelium only one cell thick

very small lumen

nucleus of cell

1) Capillaries deliver food and oxygen direct to the body tissues and take waste products away.
2) Their walls are usually only one cell thick to make it easy for stuff to pass in and out of them.
3) They are too small to see.

Veins Take Blood Back to The Heart

1) Veins carry deoxygenated blood back to the heart.
2) The blood is at lower pressure in the veins so the walls do not need to be so thick.
3) They have a bigger lumen than arteries to help blood flow.
4) They also have valves to help keep the blood flowing in the right direction.

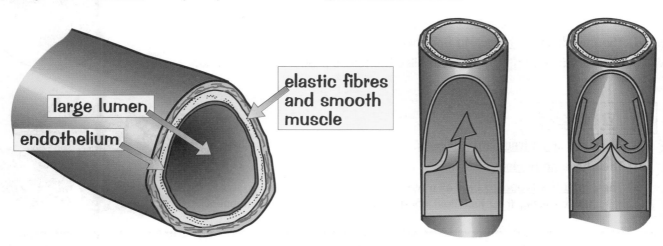

large lumen

elastic fibres and smooth muscle

endothelium

Don't struggle in vain...

Let's face it these are mighty easy diagrams to learn. Just make sure you learn the numbered points as well. I reckon it can't take more than two or three attempts before you can scribble out the whole of this page, diagrams and all, entirely from memory. Concentrate on learning the bits you forgot each time, of course. Try it and see how right I am!

Module BD1 — Supplying the Cell   OCR STAGED ASSESSMENT

Blood

There are four main constituents of blood. And guess what — you have to learn them.

Plasma

This is a pale straw-coloured liquid which carries just about everything:
1) Red and white blood cells and platelets.
2) Digested food products like glucose and amino acids.
3) Carbon dioxide from the organs to the lungs.
4) Urea from the liver to the kidneys.
5) Hormones.
6) Antibodies (including antitoxins) produced by the white blood cells.
7) Water.

Red Blood Cells

1) Their job is to carry oxygen from the lungs to all the cells in the body.

2) They have a squashed disc shape to give maximum surface area for absorbing oxygen.

3) They contain haemoglobin which is very red, and which contains a lot of iron.

4) In the lungs, haemoglobin absorbs oxygen to become oxyhaemoglobin. In body tissues the reverse happens to release oxygen to the cells.

5) Red blood cells have no nucleus (they just don't need one).

White Blood Cells

1) Their main role is defence against disease.
2) They have a big nucleus.
3) They gobble up unwelcome microorganisms.
4) They produce antibodies to fight bacteria.
5) They produce antitoxins to neutralise the toxins produced by bacteria.

Platelets

1) These are small fragments of cells.
2) They have no nucleus.
3) They help the blood to clot at a wound.
    (So basically they just float about waiting for accidents to happen!)

More blood, sweat and tears...

Do the same as usual — learn the facts until you can write them down from memory.

Just in case you think all this formal learning is a waste of time, how do you think you'd get on with these typical Exam questions if you didn't learn it all first?

Three typical Exam questions:
1) What is the function of blood plasma? (4 marks)
2) What do white blood cells do?   (3 marks)
3) What is the function of haemoglobin? (4 marks)

Revision Summary for Module BD1

Phew, there's a lot of stuff to learn in this module. And it's all that grisly "open heart surgery" type stuff too, with all those gory diagrams. Mind you, it's all fairly straightforward and factual — you know, nothing difficult to understand, just lots of facts to learn. And lots of gory diagrams. You know the big plan with these questions though. Keep practising till you can whizz them all off without a moment's hesitation on any of them. It's a nice trick if you can do it.

1) Draw a typical animal cell and put labels on it.
2) Now draw a typical plant cell and put labels on it.
3) How are red blood cells specialised for their function? What about leaf palisade cells?
4) Sketch a diagram of the digestive system and put the eight labels on it.
5) Write down at least one detail for each of the eight labelled parts.
6) What is the first stage of physical digestion?
7) What exactly do enzymes do in the digestive system?
8) What are the three "big" food molecules?
   Which kind of foods are each of them found in?
9) What small molecules are they each broken down into in the digestive system?
10) Sketch a diagram showing what then happens to the small molecules.
11) Draw a diagram of a peristaltic squeeze. Label the different types of tissue and say what they do.
12) Sketch a villus, and say what it's for. Point out the three main features of villi.
13) Sketch the graph for enzyme activity vs temperature.
14) What two things does bile do? Where is it produced?
   Where does it enter the system?
15) Draw a diagram of the thorax, showing all the breathing equipment.
16) Describe what happens during breathing in and breathing out.
   Be sure to give all the details.
17) What's the name of the process in which oxygen enters and leaves the blood?
18) Where are alveoli found? How big are they and what are they for?
19) Explain what happens to oxygen and carbon dioxide, both at alveoli and at body cells.
20) Draw a diagram of the human circulatory system: heart, lungs, arteries, veins, etc.
21) Explain why it is a double circulatory system, and describe the pressure and oxygen content of the blood in each bit.
22) What are the big words for saying if the blood has oxygen in or not?
23) What's the advantage of having a double circulatory system?
24) Draw a full diagram of the heart with all the labels. Explain how the two halves differ.
25) How do ventricles and atria compare, and why? What are the valves for?
26) Write down the word equation for the reaction of oxygen with haemoglobin.
27) Describe what happens with oxygen and haemoglobin in a) the lungs b) the tissues.
28) Sketch an artery, a capillary, and a vein, with labels, and explain the features of all three.
29) Sketch a white blood cell and give five details about it.
30) Sketch some blood plasma. List all the things that are carried in the plasma (around 10).
31) Sketch some platelets. What do they do all day?

The Nervous System

Sense Organs and Receptors

THE FIVE SENSE ORGANS ARE:
Eyes ears nose tongue skin

These five different sense organs all contain different receptors.

Receptors are groups of cells which are sensitive to a stimulus such as light or heat, etc.

SENSE ORGANS and RECEPTORS
Don't get them mixed up:

The EYE is a SENSE ORGAN — it contains LIGHT RECEPTORS (rods and cones).
The EAR is a SENSE ORGAN — it contains SOUND RECEPTORS.

RECEPTORS are cells which TRANSDUCE energy (eg. light energy) into ELECTRICAL IMPULSES.

'Transduce' means to change from one form of energy to another.

THE CENTRAL NERVOUS SYSTEM.
Consists of the brain and spinal cord only.

MOTOR NEURONES
The nerve fibres that carry signals to the effector muscle or gland.

The FIVE SENSE ORGANS and the receptors that each one contains:

1) EYES
Light receptors.

2) EARS
Sound and "balance" receptors.

3) NOSE
Taste and smell receptors (Chemical stimuli).

4) TONGUE
Taste receptors:
Bitter, salt, sweet and sour (Chemical stimuli).

5) SKIN
Touch, pressure and temperature receptors.

SENSORY NEURONES
The nerve fibres that carry signals from the receptors in the sense organs to the central nervous system.

EFFECTORS
All your muscles and glands will respond to nervous impulses.

The Central Nervous System and Effectors

1) THE CENTRAL NERVOUS SYSTEM is where all the sensory information is sent and where reflexes and actions are coordinated. It consists of THE BRAIN and SPINAL CORD only.
2) NEURONES (nerve cells) transmit electrical impulses very quickly around the body.
3) The EFFECTORS are muscles and glands which can respond to the various stimuli according to the instructions sent from the central nervous system.

This stuff is easy — I mean it's all just common senses...
There's quite a few names to learn here (as ever!).
But there's no drivel. It's all worth marks in the Exam, so learn it all.
Practise until you can cover the page and scribble down all the details from memory.

Neurones and Reflexes

The Three Types of Neurone are All Much The Same

The THREE TYPES of NEURONE are:

(They're all pretty much the same, they're just connected to different things, that's all.)

1) SENSORY neurone,
2) MOTOR neurone
3) RELAY neurone (or CONNECTOR neurone).

A Typical Neurone:

Learn the names of all the bits:

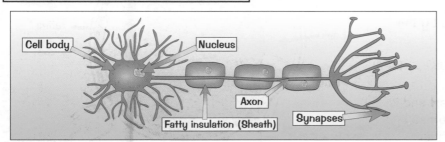

Cell body | Nucleus | Axon | Fatty insulation (Sheath) | Synapses

Neurones are pretty well adapted to the job they have to do...
1) They're long — so they can pass signals over long distances, eg. from your finger to your spine.
2) They're insulated — to protect the signal.
3) They have branched endings — to allow them to connect to lots of other neurones.

The Reflex Arc Allows Very Quick Responses

A Typical Reflex Arc

5. Message travels along a motor neurone

4. Message is passed along a relay neurone

6. When message reaches muscle, it contracts

!... OW!

3. Message travels along the sensory neurone

2. Stimulation of the pain receptor

1. Cheeky bee stings finger

A REFLEX ARC is simple enough. It's called an "arc" rather than a loop because the two ends don't connect.

1) The nervous system allows very quick responses because it uses electrical impulses.
2) Reflex actions are ones that you do without thinking so they are even quicker.
3) Reflex actions save your body from injury, eg. pulling your hand off a hot object for you.
4) The brain isn't involved in a reflex action, but it does eventually receive information about what's happened and which part of the body was affected.
5) If the brain never received this information, you wouldn't be able to remember what had happened (and you might do the same thing again).

Synapses Use Chemicals

1) The connection between two neurones is called a synapse.
2) The nerve signal is transferred by chemicals which diffuse across the gap.
3) These chemicals then set off a new electrical signal in the next neurone.

A Synapse

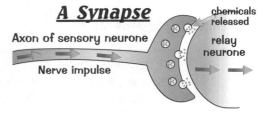

Axon of sensory neurone

Nerve impulse

chemicals released

relay neurone

Make sure you also learn the BLOCK DIAGRAM of a Reflex Arc:

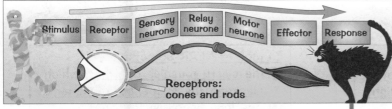

Stimulus | Receptor | Sensory neurone | Relay neurone | Motor neurone | Effector | Response

Receptors: cones and rods

(Does everyone's mummy scare them like this? — thought so.)

Don't get all twitchy — just learn it...

Another jolly page to learn, but it's all good clean fun. Once again, everything on this page is important information that you definitely need to know for the Exams. Use the diagrams to help you remember the important details. Then cover the page and scribble it all down.

Higher

The Eye

Learn The Eye with all its labels:

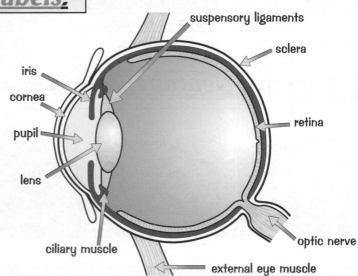

1) The tough outer sclera has a transparent region at the front called the cornea, which refracts (ie. bends) light onto the lens.

2) The pupil is the hole in the middle of the iris which the light goes through.

3) The size of the pupil is controlled by the muscular iris.

4) The lens is held in position by suspensory ligaments and ciliary muscles.

5) The retina is the light sensitive part and is covered in receptor cells. The cornea and lens produce an image on the retina.

6) Receptor cells send impulses to the brain along neurones in the optic nerve.

Adjusting for Light and Dark — the IRIS

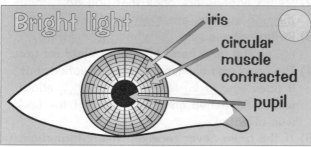

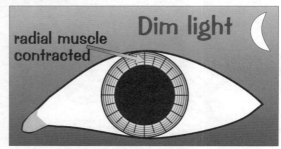

1) The circular muscles contract.
2) The iris closes up, the pupil gets smaller.
3) Less light gets into the eye.

1) The radial muscles contract.
2) The iris opens out, the pupil gets bigger.
3) This lets more light into the eye.

Focusing on Near and Distant Objects

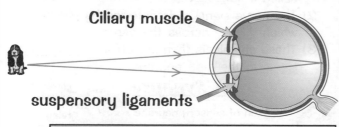

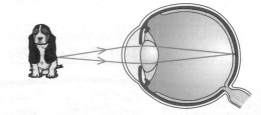

To look at DISTANT objects:
1) The ciliary muscles relax, which allows the suspensory ligaments to pull tight.
2) This makes the lens go thin.

To look at NEAR objects:
1) The ciliary muscles contract, which slackens the suspensory ligaments.
2) The lens becomes fat.

Let's see what you've learned then...

This is a straightforward page of information. Make sure you know the diagrams with all the labels and also the points for each. Practise until you can scribble the whole lot down from memory.

Hormones

Hormones are Chemical Messengers sent in the Blood

1) Hormones are chemicals released directly into the blood.
2) They are carried in the blood to other parts of the body.
3) They are produced in various glands (endocrine glands) as shown on the diagram.
4) They travel all over the body but only affect particular cells in particular places.
5) They travel at "the speed of blood".
6) They have long-lasting effects.
7) They control things that need constant adjustment.

> **Learn this definition:**
>
> HORMONES ...
> are chemical messengers
> which travel in the blood
> to activate target cells.

The Pituitary Gland

This produces many important hormones: LH, FSH and ADH. These tend to control other glands, as a rule.

Growth hormone (GH) is also produced here.

Pancreas

Produces insulin and glucagon for the control of blood sugar.

Ovaries — females only

Produce oestrogen, which causes build-up of the uterus wall and promotes all female secondary sexual characteristics during puberty:
1) Extra hair in places.
2) Changes in body proportions.
3) Egg production.
Progesterone is also made here — this maintains the uterus wall. Oestrogen and progesterone together control ovulation.

Thyroid

This controls the body's metabolism by releasing thyroxine into the blood.

Adrenal Gland

Produces adrenaline, which prepares the body with the well known fight or flight reaction:
Increased blood sugar, heart rate, breathing rate, and diversion of blood from skin to muscles.

Kidney

Testes — males only

Produce testosterone, which promotes all male secondary sexual characteristics at puberty:
1) Extra hair in places.
2) Changes in body proportions.
3) Sperm production.
4) Lower voice.

Hormones and Nerves do Similar Jobs but there are Important Differences

Nerves:
1) Very fast message.
2) Act for a very short time.
3) Act on a very precise area.
4) Immediate reaction.

Hormones:
1) Slower message.
2) Act for a long time.
3) Act in a more general way.
4) Longer-term reaction.

Hormones — Easy peasy...

Well, let's face it, there's not much to learn here is there? The diagram and its labels are easy enough, and so's the comparison of nerves and hormones. The definition of hormones is worth learning word for word. The seven points at the top of the page are best done with the good old mini-essay method. Learn it, cover the page and scribble. Then try again.

Module B02 — Control in Animals and Plants   OCR STAGED ASSESSMENT

Hormone Treatments

Insulin Controls Blood Sugar Levels

1) Eating carbohydrate foods puts a lot of glucose into the blood from the gut.
2) Normal metabolism of cells removes glucose from the blood.
3) Vigorous exercise removes much more glucose from the blood.
4) Obviously, to keep the level of blood glucose controlled there has to be a way to add or remove glucose from the blood.
5) If blood glucose is too high, insulin is released which converts the excess glucose to glycogen in the liver. (This can be converted back into glucose when sugar levels drop too low.)

Diabetes — the Pancreas Stops Making Enough Insulin

1) Diabetes is a disease in which the pancreas doesn't produce enough insulin.
2) The result is that a person's blood sugar can rise to a level that can kill them.
3) The problem can be controlled in two ways:

   A) Avoiding foods rich in carbohydrate (which turns to glucose when digested). It can also be helpful to take exercise after eating carbohydrates... ie. try to use up the extra glucose by doing physical activity, but this isn't usually very practical.

   B) INJECTING INSULIN INTO THE BLOOD before meals, (especially if high in carbohydrates). This will make the liver remove the glucose from the blood as soon as it enters it from the gut, when the (carbohydrate-rich) food is being digested. This stops the level of glucose in the blood from getting too high and is a very effective treatment, although the amount of insulin needed has to be specifically matched to a person's diet and activity level.

Hormones are Used to Control Fertility and Growth

FSH is Used to Stimulate Egg Production in Fertility Treatment

1) A hormone called FSH can be taken by women to stimulate egg production in their ovaries.
2) In fact FSH (Follicle Stimulating Hormone) stimulates the ovaries to produce oestrogen which in turn stimulates the release of an egg.
3) But you do have to be careful with the dosage or you get too many eggs, resulting in multiple births.

Oestrogen is Used to Stop Egg Production in "The PILL"

1) "THE PILL", as it's cheerfully known, contains both progesterone and oestrogen.
2) It may seem kind of strange but even though oestrogen stimulates the release of eggs, if oestrogen is taken every day to keep the level of it permanently high, it inhibits the production of FSH and after a while egg production stops and stays stopped.

HGH Replacement Therapy helps Some Children Grow Properly

1) Some children are born with too little human growth hormone (HGH).
2) If untreated, the child grows very slowly, and never reaches normal height.
3) In many cases, the problem can be treated with HGH made in the lab.
4) The hormone replacement therapy works very well — but the patient needs to take drugs every day until the end of adolescence.
5) HGH also has other uses — particularly in anti-ageing treatments.

...but Some People use Hormones for Less Worthy Causes

Some athletes use hormones (illegally) to improve performance — usually anabolic steroids which are based on testosterone. They increase muscle growth and also make the athlete more aggressive.

Testosterone — more trouble than you can shake a stick at...

You need to learn all this stuff about hormones. Don't try and learn it all in one go. Take it one section at a time. See how much you can write down from memory, then check yourself.

Plant Hormones

Hormones control many key processes in plants including root and shoot growth. In particular, they makes roots and shoots grow in the right direction.

Auxins are Plant Growth Hormones

1) Auxins are hormones which control growth at the tips of shoots and roots.

2) Auxin is produced in the tips and diffuses backwards in solution to stimulate the cell elongation process which occurs in the cells just behind the tips.

3) If the tip of a shoot is removed, no auxin will be available and the shoot may stop growing.

4) Shoot tips also produce substances which inhibit the growth of side shoots. If the tips are removed it can result in a lot of side shoots because the inhibitor substance is no longer present. Hence, hedge clipping promotes bushier hedges, because it produces lots of side shoots.

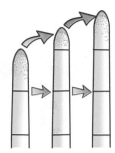

Auxins Change The Direction of Shoot Growth

You'll note below that extra auxin promotes growth in the shoot but actually inhibits growth in the root — but also note that this produces the desired result in both cases.

1) Shoots bend towards the light

1) This is called phototropism.

2) When a shoot tip is exposed to light, it provides more auxin on the side that is in the shade than the side which is in the light.

3) This causes the shoot to grow faster on the shaded side and it bends towards the light.

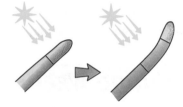

2) Roots bend towards Gravity

1) This is geotropism.

2) A root growing sideways will experience the same redistribution of auxin to the lower side.

3) But in a root the extra auxin actually inhibits growth, causing it to bend downwards instead.

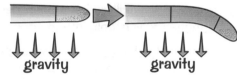

gravity   gravity

3) Auxin is Produced in the Tip of a Shoot

Learn this experiment with auxins and shoot tips.

1) Cover the tip of one plant shoot with a lightproof cap, and bury another in black sand with only the tip showing.

2) When light is shone at both shoots, only the one with the tip showing bends towards the light — showing that it's the tip that's sensitive to light because that's where the auxin is being produced.

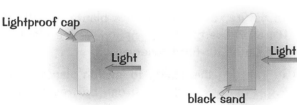

Lightproof cap

Light

Light

black sand

Just a few tips for your revision...

An easy page to learn. Just four points on auxins, together with a diagram, and then info on how shoots and roots change direction, with a diagram for each. You just have to learn it. Then cover the page and scribble down the main points from memory. Then try again...

Module BD2 — Control in Animals and Plants   OCR STAGED ASSESSMENT

Commercial Uses of Hormones

Plant hormones have a lot of uses in the <u>food growing business</u>.

1) Controlling the Ripening of Fruit

1) The <u>ripening</u> of fruits can be controlled either while they are <u>still on the plant</u>, or during <u>transport</u> to the shops.

2) This allows the fruit to be picked while it's still <u>unripe</u> (and therefore firmer and <u>less easily damaged</u>).

3) It can then be sprayed with <u>ripening hormone</u> and it will ripen <u>on the way</u> to the supermarket to be perfect just as it reaches the shelves.

2) Growing from Cuttings with Rooting Compound

1) A <u>cutting</u> is part of a plant that has been <u>cut off</u>, like the end of a branch with a few leaves on it.

2) Normally, if you stick cuttings in the soil they <u>won't grow</u>, but if you add <u>rooting compound</u>, which is a plant <u>growth hormone</u>, they will produce roots rapidly and start growing as <u>new plants</u>.

3) This enables growers to produce lots of <u>clones</u> (exact copies) of a really good plant <u>very quickly</u>.

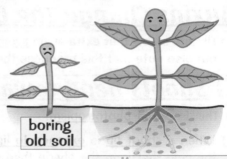

boring old soil

rooting compound

3) Killing Weeds

1) Most weeds growing in fields of crops or in a lawn are <u>broad-leaved</u>, in contrast to grass which has very <u>narrow leaves</u>.

2) <u>Selective weedkillers</u> have been developed from <u>plant growth hormones</u> which only affect broad-leaved plants.

3) They totally <u>disrupt</u> their normal <u>growth patterns</u>, which soon <u>kills</u> them, whilst leaving the grass untouched.

Unhappy weeds

4) Control of Dormancy

1) <u>Dormancy</u> in plants (when they're alive but not doing anything) is affected by hormones called <u>growth regulators</u>.

2) In nature, dormancy allows plants to withstand cold winters or food shortages. It's a bit like <u>plant hibernation</u> — the plant kind of 'switches off' so that it doesn't use up all its food reserves.

3) In <u>industry</u> this ability to 'switch plants on and off' can be put to use. E.g. <u>Potatoes</u> and <u>barley</u> can be treated so that they don't <u>sprout</u> during storage.

Remember, serious learning always bears fruit...

Another blissfully easy page. Just make sure you learn enough about each bit to answer a 3 mark Exam question on it (that means being able to make 3 valid points). As usual the sections are split into numbered points to help you remember them. They've all got three points to learn. <u>So learn them</u>. Then <u>cover the page</u> and <u>scribble down</u> the 3 points for each .

Revision Summary for Module BD2

This module isn't too bad really. Well, it's short for one thing. That always helps. It makes things a lot quicker if you make good use of all the pictures — these are far easier to remember than just lists and lists of facts. Once you know the pictures, try to tag on the extra info you need to know. You'll soon find that simply drawing the picture brings all the detail back to you. Same drill as usual with these questions — keep going 'til you know the lot.

1) Draw a diagram showing the main parts of the nervous system.
2) What are receptors and effectors?
3) List the five sense organs and say what kind of receptors each one has.
4) What two things constitute the central nervous system?
5) What are the three different types of neurone?
6) Draw a diagram of a typical neurone. Explain why it's well suited to the job it has to do.
7) Describe how a reflex arc works.
8) Draw and label a synapse. How do they work?
9) Sketch a diagram of an eye and fully label it.
10) What does each part of the eye do?
11) Using diagrams, show how the eye adjusts to light and dark.
12) Describe how the eye focuses on near and distant objects.
13) Draw a diagram of the body and label the six places where hormones are produced. Name the hormones produced at each place and say what they do.
14) Give the proper definition of hormones.
15) What is an endocrine gland?
16) Give four details to compare hormones with nerves.
17) Explain what happens with insulin when the blood sugar is too high and when it is too low.
18) What is diabetes? Describe the two ways that it can be controlled, and compare their effectiveness.
19) Give three other examples of hormone treatments.
20) What hormones are used in the contraceptive pill, and how does it work?
21) Give an example of an illegal use of hormones.
22) What are auxins? Where are they produced?
23) Explain why clipping a hedge promotes bushier growth.
24) Name the two ways that auxins affect roots and shoots. Give full details for them.
25) List four commercial uses for plant hormones.
26) Why are ripening hormones useful?
27) Explain what rooting compound is used for.
28) How do hormonal weed killers work?
29) Give an example of an industrial use of hormones that control plant dormancy.

Counting Methods and Sampling

One ant, two ants, three ants, four ants, five ants — rats, lost count. One ant, two ants...

Collecting and Counting Organisms

You need to know about various pieces of kit you can use to collect or count animals.

1) A QUADRAT is a square frame

Quadrats are usually 1m² in area.

You put the quadrat on the ground and count everything inside it.

They're used to estimate population sizes — see below.

2) NETS are for catching small animals

Nets can be used for catching flying insects or small sea creatures.

3) PIT-FALL traps catch animals

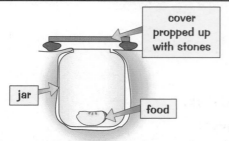

cover propped up with stones

jar

food

The animal is attracted by the food, crawls under the cover and falls into the jar.

The cover stops rain getting in.

4) POOTERS suck up small animals like insects

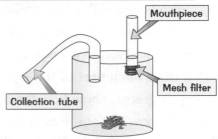

Mouthpiece

Mesh filter

Collection tube

You point the collection tube at an animal and suck on the mouthpiece. The animal gets sucked up the collection tube into the jar.

The mesh filter stops it ending up in your mouth.

Estimate Population Sizes using a Quadrat

1) First you have to count the organisms in a 1m² quadrat.
2) Then you multiply the number of organisms by the total area (in m²) of the habitat.
3) Er, that's it. Bob's your uncle.

Example: Estimate the total populations of the various species in a 120m² meadow if a 1m² quadrat contained 90 grass plants, 30 buttercups, 25 daisies, 6 poppies and 3 cornflowers.

Answer: Multiply the figures for the 1m² quadrat by 120 to estimate the populations in the whole meadow. So the meadow will contain about 10 800 grass plants, 3 600 buttercups, 3 000 daisies, 720 poppies and 360 cornflowers.

These Counting Methods have Two Limitations

1) The sample size affects the accuracy of the estimate — the bigger your sample, the more accurate your estimate of the total population is likely to be.
So to get an estimate of the population of a 500m² habitat, it'd be better to take ten 1m² quadrats and multiply the result by 50 rather than take only one 1m² quadrat and multiply the result by 500.

2) The sample may not be representative of the population, ie. what you find in your quadrat might be different to what you'd have found if you'd looked somewhere else. To get a better idea of what's in the whole habitat, it's better to use 10 quadrats scattered over a wide area than 10 close together.

Counting methods — DON'T avoid the pit-falls...

You could be asked how you'd collect data to make an estimate of the size of a population. It's not hard really, but you need to remember the limitations of the quadrat method. Learn all this properly now and you'll be laughing when it comes up in the exam...

Population Sizes

POPULATION SIZE just means how many of <u>one type of plant or animal</u> there is in a given ecosystem, and more importantly, <u>WHY ONLY THAT MANY</u>, why not more? The answer is that there are always <u>LIMITING FACTORS</u>, such as <u>too little food</u> or <u>too many other animals</u> eating the food as well, or <u>too many animals eating them</u>, etc... This can all start to get out of hand and sound really complicated. But it's <u>really very simple</u>, and you must keep telling yourself that!

Limits on Animal and Plant Populations

<u>Approach 1</u> — the size of the population of any animal or plant is due to <u>SEVEN FACTORS</u>:

1) The <u>TOTAL AMOUNT OF FOOD</u> or nutrients available (including <u>MINERALS</u> in the case of plants).
2) The amount of <u>WATER</u> available.
3) The amount of <u>COMPETITION</u> there is (from other species) for the same food or nutrients.
4) The <u>AMOUNT OF LIGHT AVAILABLE</u> (this applies only to plants really).
5) The quality and amount of <u>SHELTER</u> available.
6) The <u>NUMBER OF PREDATORS</u> (or grazers) who may eat the animal (or plant) in question.
7) <u>DISEASE</u>.

<u>Approach 2</u> — the size of the population of any animal or plant is due to <u>THREE FACTORS</u>:

1) <u>ADAPTATION</u> — how well the animal has become <u>adapted to its environment</u>.
2) <u>COMPETITION</u> — how well the animal <u>competes with other species</u> for the same food.
3) <u>PREDATION</u> — how well the animal <u>avoids being eaten</u>.

In the Exam they could ask you about it from either viewpoint. Although these lists seem kind of hard to relate to, what they're saying is surely just common sense ...

In other words... organisms will thrive best if:

1) <u>THERE'S PLENTY OF THE GOOD THINGS IN LIFE</u>: food, water, space, shelter, light, etc.
2) <u>THEY'RE BETTER THAN THE COMPETITION AT GETTING IT</u> (better adapted).
3) <u>THEY DON'T GET EATEN</u>.
4) <u>THEY DON'T GET ILL</u>.

That's pretty much the long and the short of it, wouldn't you say? So learn those four things. Every species is different, of course, but those <u>FOUR</u> basic principles will always apply. In Exam questions <u>YOU</u> have to apply them to any new situation to work out what'll happen.

Populations of Prey and Predators go in Cycles

In a community containing prey and predators (as most of them do of course):

1) The <u>POPULATION</u> of any species is usually <u>limited</u> by the amount of <u>FOOD</u> available.
2) If the population of the <u>PREY</u> increases, then so will the population of the <u>PREDATORS</u>.
3) However as the population of predators <u>INCREASES</u>, the number of prey will <u>DECREASE</u>.

ie. <u>More grass</u> means <u>more rabbits</u>.
More rabbits means <u>more foxes</u>.
But more foxes means <u>fewer rabbits</u>.
Eventually fewer rabbits will mean <u>fewer foxes again</u>.
This <u>up and down pattern</u> continues...

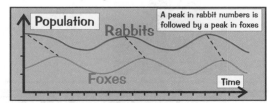

Revision stress — don't let it eat you up...

It's a strange topic is population sizes. In a way it seems like common sense, but it all seems to get so messy. Anyway, <u>learn all the points on this page</u> and you'll be OK with it, I'd think.

Producers, Consumers and Parasites

A Woodland Food Web

Food webs are pretty easy really. Hideously easy in fact.

1) A food chain is just part of a food web, starting at the bottom and following the arrows up.

2) Remember, the arrows show which way the food energy travels.

3) Don't mix up who eats who either! The arrow means "IS EATEN BY", so you follow the arrow to the one doing the eating.

4) From the woodland food web we could take this food chain:

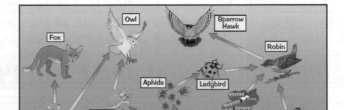

Terminology you need to know

1) **PRODUCER** — all plants are producers. They use the sun's energy to produce food energy.
2) **HERBIVORE** — animals which only eat plants, eg. rabbits, caterpillars, aphids.
3) **CONSUMER** — all animals are consumers. All plants are not, because they are producers.
4) **PRIMARY CONSUMER** — animal which eats producers (plants).
5) **SECONDARY CONSUMER** — animal which eats primary consumers.
6) **TERTIARY CONSUMER** — animal which eats secondary consumers.
7) **CARNIVORE** — eats only animals, never plants.
8) **TOP CARNIVORE** — is not eaten by anything else, except decomposers after it dies.
9) **OMNIVORE** — eats both plants and animals.
10) **PARASITE** — a plant or animal which lives on or in a host plant or animal, and feeds on the host.
11) **DECOMPOSER** — lives off all dead material — producers, consumers, top carnivore, the lot.

Parasites and mutualistic relationships

The survival of some organisms can depend almost entirely on the presence of other species. This dependence can have two different forms: parasites and mutualistic relationships.

1) Parasites live off a host. They take what they need to survive without giving anything back. Fleas are parasites. Dogs gain nothing from having fleas.
2) In a mutualistic relationship, both organisms gain. One of the exam board's favourite examples of a mutualistic relationship is root nodules in leguminous plants.

Root nodules containing nitrogen-fixing bacteria

Most plants have to rely on nitrogen-fixing bacteria in the soil to get the nitrates that they need. But leguminous plants (such as beans) carry the bacteria in nodules in their roots.

The bacteria get a constant supply of nutrients from the plant, and the plant gets essential nitrates from the bacteria. It's a win-win situation.

Learn about Food Webs, terminology and all...

Don't get too stressed about all those definitions — all you have to do is learn them. Also, make sure you get your head round the difference between parasites and mutualistic relationships — and learn an example of each. Then cover the page and scribble it all down.

Pyramids of Number and Biomass

This is hideously easy too. Just <u>make sure you know</u> what <u>all</u> the pyramids mean.

Each Level you go up, there's fewer of them...

<u>5000</u> dandelions...   feed..   <u>100</u> rabbits...   which feed....   <u>one</u> fox.

<u>In other words</u>, each time you go <u>up one level</u> the <u>number of organisms goes down</u> — <u>a lot</u>.
It takes <u>a lot</u> of food from the level <u>below</u> to keep any one animal alive.
This gives us the good old <u>number pyramid</u>:

> 1 Fox
> 100 Rabbits
> 5,000 Dandelions

This is the <u>basic idea</u> anyway. But there are cases where the pyramid is <u>not a pyramid at all</u>:

Number Pyramids Sometimes Look Wrong

This is a <u>pyramid</u> except for the <u>top layer</u> which goes <u>huge</u>:

> 500 Fleas
> 1 Fox
> 100 Rabbits
> 5,000 Dandelions

This is a <u>pyramid</u> apart from the <u>bottom layer</u> which is <u>way too small</u>:

> 1 Partridge
> 1000 Ladybirds
> 3,000 Aphids
> 1 Pear tree

Biomass Pyramids Never Look Wrong

When <u>number pyramids</u> seem to go <u>wrong</u> like this, then the good old <u>pyramid of biomass</u> comes to the rescue. <u>Biomass</u> is just how much all the creatures at each level would "weigh" if you <u>put them all together</u>. So the <u>one pear tree</u> would have a <u>big biomass</u> and the <u>hundreds of fleas</u> would have <u>a very small biomass</u>. Biomass pyramids are <u>always the right shape</u>:

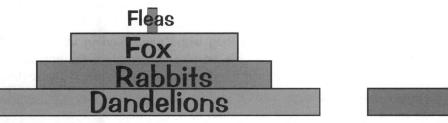

> Fleas
> Fox
> Rabbits
> Dandelions

> Partridge
> Ladybirds
> Aphids
> Pear tree

Basically, <u>biomass pyramids</u> are the only <u>sensible</u> way to do it — it's just that <u>number pyramids</u> are <u>easier to understand</u>.

Now Children, get your coloured wooden blocks out...

...hideously easy...

Energy From the Sun

All that *Energy* just *Disappears* Somehow...

1) Energy from the SUN is the source of energy for all life on Earth.
2) Plants convert a small % of the light energy that falls on them into glucose.
3) This energy then works its way through the food web.
4) But 90% is lost at each stage — 90% of biomass and 90% of energy content.
5) So the rabbits contain only 10% of the total chemical energy (food energy) of the dandelions.
6) This explains why you get biomass pyramids. Most of the biomass from each level does not become biomass in the next level up.
7) The 90% of the ENERGY lost at each stage is used for staying alive, ie. in respiration, which powers all life processes, including movement.
8) Most of this energy is eventually lost to the surroundings as heat.
9) This is especially true for mammals and birds which keep themselves warm (ie. are warm-blooded). They eat a lot more food than creatures which don't. A pet goldfish is cold-blooded and only seems to need about 1/100th the amount of food that a pet mouse needs.
10) The 90% of the FOOD MATTER lost at each stage is passed out mostly as faeces.
11) Think about a rabbit. Once it's fully grown it carries on eating greens but its biomass doesn't change, and neither does its energy value to whatever finally eats it.
12) All the biomass it eats must be lost from its body somehow, or it would get bigger. Most gets egested (passed out) in the droppings.
13) And once fully grown, all the energy it consumes is just used for keeping it alive, and none of it will pass on down the food chain.
14) Some energy is also lost from the food chain in the droppings — they burn when dried, proving they still have chemical energy in them.

Try it next time you're camping — you'll find you enjoy your midnight sausages that much more when they're cooked over a blazing mound of dried sheep poo.

Two Ways to Improve the "Efficiency" of Food Production

1) *Reducing* the Number of Stages in *Food Chains*

1) For a given area of land, you can produce a lot more food (for humans) by growing crops rather than by grazing animals. This is because you are reducing the number of stages in the food chain. Only 10% of what beef cattle eat becomes useful meat for people to eat.

2) However, don't forget that just eating crops can quickly lead to malnutrition through lack of essential proteins and minerals, unless a varied enough diet is achieved. Also remember that some land is unsuitable for growing crops, such as moorland or fellsides. In these places, animals like sheep and deer are often the best way to get food from the land.

2) *Restricting* the Energy Lost by *Farm Animals*

1) In 'civilised' countries such as ours, animals like pigs and chickens are reared in strict conditions of limited movement and artificial warmth, in order to reduce their energy losses to a minimum.

2) In other words keep them still enough and hot enough and they won't need feeding as much. It's as simple and as horrible as that. If you deny them even the simplest of simple pleasures in their short little stay on this planet before you eat them, then it won't cost you as much in feed. Lovely.

3) But intensively reared animals like chickens and pigs, kept in a little shed all their life, still require land indirectly because they still need feeding, so land is needed to grow their "feed" on. So would it be so terrible to let them have a little corner of it in the sunshine somewhere, huh...?

Locked up in a little cage with no sunlight — who'd work in a bank...

Phew! Just look at all those words crammed onto one page. Geesh.... I mean blimey, it almost looks like a page from a normal science book. Almost. Anyway, there it all is, on the page, waiting to be blended with the infinite void inside your head. Learn and enjoy... and scribble.

Decomposition and the Carbon Cycle

1) <u>Living things</u> are made of materials they take from the world around them.
2) When they <u>decompose</u>, ashes are returned to ashes, and dust to dust, as it were.
3) In other words the <u>elements</u> they contain are returned to the <u>soil</u> where they came from <u>originally</u>.
4) These elements are then <u>used by plants</u> to grow and the whole cycle <u>repeats</u> over and over again.

Decomposition *is carried out by* Bacteria *and* Fungi

1) All <u>plant matter</u> and <u>dead animals</u> are broken down (digested) by <u>microbes</u>.
2) This happens everywhere in <u>nature</u>, and also in <u>compost heaps</u> and <u>sewage works</u>.
3) All the important <u>elements</u> are thus <u>recycled</u>:
   <u>Carbon</u>, <u>Hydrogen</u>, <u>Oxygen</u> and <u>Nitrogen</u>.
4) The <u>ideal conditions</u> for creating <u>compost</u> are:
   a) <u>WARMTH</u>
   b) <u>MOISTURE</u>
   c) <u>OXYGEN (AIR)</u>
   d) <u>MICROORGANISMS</u> (<u>bacteria</u> and <u>fungi</u>)
   e) <u>ORGANIC MATTER</u> cut into <u>small pieces</u>.
   Make sure you <u>learn them</u> — <u>all five</u>.

Extra microbes added (compost maker)

Finely shredded waste is best

Warmth generated by decomposition helps it all along

Mesh sides to let air in

There's a bloke I know, and everyone calls him "the party mushroom". I'm not sure why really — they just say he's a fun guy to be with...

The Carbon Cycle *Shows how* Carbon *is* Recycled

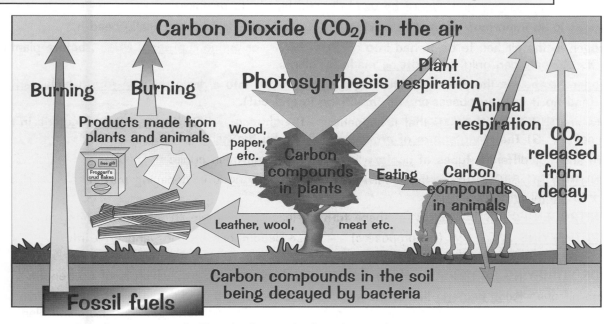

Carbon Dioxide (CO₂) in the air

Burning   Burning   Photosynthesis   Plant respiration   Animal respiration   CO₂ released from decay

Products made from plants and animals

Wood, paper, etc.

Carbon compounds in plants

Eating

Carbon compounds in animals

Leather, wool,   meat etc.

Carbon compounds in the soil being decayed by bacteria

Fossil fuels

This diagram isn't half as bad as it looks. <u>Learn</u> these important points:
1) There's only <u>one arrow</u> going <u>down</u>. The whole thing is "powered" by <u>photosynthesis</u>.
2) Both plant and animal <u>respiration</u> put CO₂ <u>back into the atmosphere</u>.
3) <u>Plants</u> convert the carbon in <u>CO₂ from the air</u> into <u>fats</u>, <u>carbohydrates</u> and <u>proteins</u>.
4) These can then go <u>three ways</u>: <u>be eaten</u>, <u>decay</u> or be turned into <u>useful products</u> by man.
5) <u>Eating</u> transfers some of the fats, proteins and carbohydrates to <u>new</u> fats, carbohydrates and proteins <u>in the animal</u> doing the eating.
6) Ultimately these plant and animal products either <u>decay</u> or are <u>burned</u> and <u>CO₂ is released</u>.

On Ilkley Moor baht 'at, On Ilkley Moor baht 'at...

Learn the five ideal conditions for compost making. They like asking about that.
Sketch out your <u>own simplified version</u> of the carbon cycle, making sure it contains all the labels.
Practise <u>scribbling</u> it out <u>from memory</u>. And keep trying till you can do it <u>perfectly</u>.

The Nitrogen Cycle

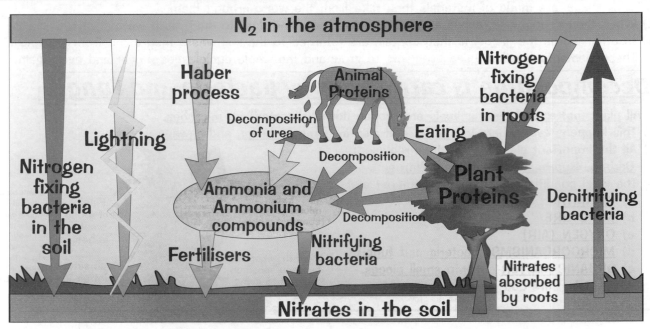

N₂ in the atmosphere

Haber process

Lightning

Nitrogen fixing bacteria in the soil

Animal Proteins

Decomposition of urea

Decomposition

Eating

Nitrogen fixing bacteria in roots

Plant Proteins

Denitrifying bacteria

Ammonia and Ammonium compounds

Fertilisers

Nitrifying bacteria

Decomposition

Nitrates absorbed by roots

Nitrates in the soil

1) The <u>atmosphere</u> contains <u>78% nitrogen gas</u>, N₂.

2) This is <u>very unreactive</u> and cannot be used directly by plants or animals.

3) <u>Nitrogen</u> is an important element in making <u>protein</u> and also <u>DNA</u>, so we really need it.

4) Nitrogen in the air has to be turned into <u>nitrates</u>, NO_3^-, or <u>ammonium ions</u>, NH_4^+, before plants can use it. <u>Animals</u> can only use <u>proteins</u> made by plants.

5) <u>Nitrogen Fixation</u> is the process of turning <u>N₂ from the air</u> into a <u>more reactive form</u> which <u>plants can use</u> (and no it isn't an obsession with breathing in and out).

6) There are <u>THREE MAIN WAYS</u> that it happens: 1) <u>Lightning</u>,   2) <u>Nitrogen-fixing bacteria</u> in roots and soil,   3) The <u>manufacture of artificial fertilisers</u> by the <u>Haber process</u>.

7) There are <u>four</u> different types of <u>bacteria</u> involved in the nitrogen cycle:

   a) <u>NITRIFYING BACTERIA</u> — these turn <u>ammonium compounds</u> in decaying matter into <u>useful nitrates</u>.

   b) <u>NITROGEN-FIXING BACTERIA</u> — these turn useless <u>atmospheric N₂</u> into useful <u>nitrates</u>.

   c) <u>PUTREFYING BACTERIA</u> (decomposers) — these decompose <u>proteins</u> and <u>urea</u> into <u>ammonia</u> or <u>ammonium compounds</u>.

   d) <u>DE-NITRIFYING BACTERIA</u> — these turn <u>nitrates</u> back into <u>N₂ gas</u>, which is of no benefit.

8) Some <u>nitrogen-fixing bacteria</u> live in the <u>soil</u>. Others live a <u>mutualistic relationship</u> with certain plants, called <u>legumes</u>, by living in <u>nodules</u> in their <u>roots</u>. The bacteria get <u>food</u> from the plant, and the plant gets <u>nitrogen compounds</u> from the bacteria — which it makes into <u>proteins</u>.

9) Any organic waste, such as rotting plants or dead animals or animal poo, will contain <u>useful nitrogen compounds</u> (proteins), so they all make <u>good fertiliser</u> if they're put back into the <u>soil</u>.

10) <u>Leguminous plants</u> (legumes) such as <u>clover</u> are useful in <u>crop rotation</u> schemes, where the field is <u>left</u> for a year to just grow <u>clover</u>, and then it's all simply <u>ploughed back into the soil</u>. This adds a lot of <u>nitrates</u> to the soil when the plants <u>decay</u>.

11) <u>Lightning</u> adds nitrates to the soil by <u>splitting up N₂</u> into nitrogen <u>atoms</u> which react with the <u>oxygen</u> in the air to form <u>oxides of nitrogen</u>. These then <u>dissolve in rain</u>, and fall to the ground where they combine with other things to form <u>nitrates</u>.

By Gum, you young 'uns have some stuff to learn...

It's really "grisly grimsdike" is the Nitrogen Cycle, I think. But the fun guys at the Exam Boards want you to know all about it, so there you go. <u>Have a good time</u>... and smile!

There Are Too Many People

There's one born every minute — and it's too many

1) The population of the world is currently rising out of control, mostly due to modern medicine and improved farming techniques.

2) The world's population is rising almost exponentially — which means it's increasing very quickly.

3) The death rate is now much lower than the birth rate in many under-developed countries, meaning there are lots more babies born than people dying.

4) This creates big problems for those countries trying to cope with all those extra people.

5) Even providing basic health care and education (especially about contraception!) is difficult, never mind finding them places to live, and food to eat.

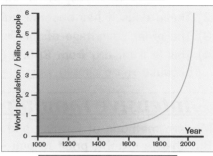

Increasing Living Standards Adds Even More Pressure

The rapidly increasing population is not the only pressure on the environment. The increasing standard of living amongst more developed countries also demands more from the environment, and although these developed countries have only a small proportion of the world's population, they cause a large proportion of the pollution. This all means that:

1) Raw materials, including non-renewable energy resources, are rapidly being used up.

2) More and more waste is being produced.

3) Unless waste is properly handled more pollution will be caused.

When the Earth's population was much smaller, the effects of human activity were usually small and local.

Waste Gases are Polluting the Environment

The burning of coal, oil and gas (fossil fuels) releases various polluting gases.

1) Burning fossil fuels releases carbon dioxide — a greenhouse gas. The Greenhouse Effect (see P50) is the most likely cause of global warming.

2) Other dodgy gases are also released when fossil fuels are burned. Sulphur dioxide reacts with the water in clouds to form an acid which then falls as acid rain. Acid rain causes lakes to become acidic, kills trees and damages buildings.

3) It's not just fossil fuels that cause problems though. CFC gases are damaging the ozone layer. This damage allows more of the Sun's UV rays through and increases the risk of skin cancer.

More People Means More Environmental Damage

Human activity can pollute all three parts of the environment:
1) Water – with sewage, fertiliser and toxic chemicals.
2) Air – with smoke and gases such as sulphur dioxide.
3) Land – with toxic chemicals, such as pesticides and herbicides. These may then be washed from the land into water.

So much to learn — so little time to learn it...

It's real scary innit — the way that graph of world population seems to be pointing nearly vertically upwards... tricky. Anyway, you just worry about your Exams instead, and make sure you know all the grim facts. Four sections — mini-essays for each, till you know it all.

Intensive Farming and Pesticides

Farming Produces a Lot of Food, Which is Great, but...

1) Farming is important to us because it allows us to produce a lot of food from less and less land.
2) These days it has become quite a high-tech industry. Food production is big business.
3) The great advantage of this is a huge variety of top quality foods, all year round, at cheap prices.
4) This is a far cry from Britain 50 years ago when food had to be rationed by the government because there simply wasn't enough for everyone. That's hard to imagine today... but try...

...Intensive Farming Can Destroy the Environment

Modern methods of farming and agriculture give us the ability to produce plenty of food for everyone. But there's a hefty price to pay — one that we're already paying. Modern Farming methods can damage the world we live in, making it polluted, unattractive and bereft of wildlife. The main effects are:

1) Removal of hedges to make huge great fields for maximum efficiency.
   This destroys the natural habitat of many wild creatures, and can lead to serious soil erosion.
2) Loss of meadowlands full of wild flowers, of natural woodlands and orchards of cherry trees, of rolling fields of grass and flowers, and tree-topped hills and leafy lanes — just swept away in a couple of decades, along with all the natural timeless beauty of rural England.
3) Careless use of fertilisers pollutes rivers and lakes, making them green, slimy and horrible.
4) Pesticides disturb food chains and reduce many insect, bird and mammal populations.
5) Intensive farming of animals such as battery-hens, and crated veal calves is simply indecent.

It is possible to farm efficiently and still maintain a healthy and beautiful environment.
But maximum profit and efficiency will have to be compromised if we are to make our countryside more than just one big industrial food factory, and also to treat our fellow creatures (many of whom we will eventually eat) with some basic level of decency and respect and humanity.

Pesticides Disturb Food Chains

1) Farmers can produce more food by using pesticides.
2) Pesticides are sprayed onto most crops to kill the various insects that can damage the crops.
3) Unfortunately, they also kill lots of harmless insects such as bees and beetles.
4) This can cause a shortage of food for many insect-eating birds.
5) Pesticides tend to be poisonous and there's always the danger of the poison passing on to other animals (as well as humans).
6) And since some pesticides are not excreted (ie. passed out of animals' bodies), they can accumulate in food chains.

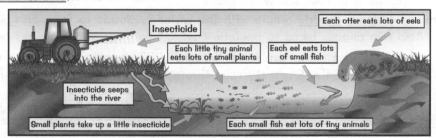

This is well illustrated by the case of otters which were almost wiped out over much of crop-dominated Southern England by a pesticide called DDT in the early 1960s. The diagram shows the food chain which ends with the otter. DDT is not excreted so it accumulates along the food chain and the otter ends up with all the DDT collected by all the other animals.

Modern farming — we're all spoiled by it...

More environment problems. This stuff can certainly get a bit tedious. At first it can be quite interesting, but then having to make sure you've learnt all those drivelly little details is not. Still, there's worse things in life than a bit of revision. So learn and enjoy. It's the only way.

Biological Pest Control

The obvious <u>advantage</u> of using biological pest control is that you don't need harmful pesticides. Nothing is without its <u>disadvantages</u> though — biological pest control takes a long time to get results.

Biological Pest Control *can take Quite a While to* Work

If you have a pest problem in your greenhouse, you could introduce <u>predators</u> to eat the trouble-causing bugs. Which predator you need depends on what you need to get rid of...

1) The <u>Aphidoletes</u> midge lays <u>larvae</u> which <u>eat aphids</u>.
2) There's a <u>special type of ladybird</u> which <u>attacks mealy bugs</u>.
3) <u>Encarsia</u> is a <u>tiny wasp</u> which lays its eggs <u>inside whitefly</u>, who then get <u>eaten from inside</u>. (Charming.)
4) There's a <u>tiny red mite</u> called <u>Phytoseiulus</u> which <u>attacks red spider mites</u>.

This kind of biological pest control can take a while to get results. The graph shows the sort of <u>time scales</u> that can be involved, and how the populations of <u>pest</u> and <u>predator</u> vary.

Both populations gradually settle down to a <u>gentle undulating pattern</u>. But notice it can take <u>18 months</u> (that's 1½ years) for the pesky bug to be brought <u>under control</u>.

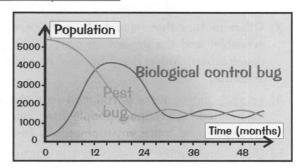

Biological Pest Control *means Tinkering* with *Food Webs*

1) Biological pest control involves introducing new animals into a system — predators to eat the pests, basically.

2) Tinkering with food webs in this way is a dodgy business — by <u>adding</u> an animal to a food chain, you affect all the others. The same goes for <u>taking</u> one away, as illustrated below.

Exam Q. — *What happens if you* take out *the* frogs...?

1) If one of the animals in this pond food web is <u>removed</u>, there'll be an effect on the <u>other</u> creatures?

2) In the Exam, you might get asked what'd happen to the number of <u>slugs</u> or <u>perch</u> if all the <u>frogs</u> were <u>removed</u>.

3) It's <u>simple enough</u>, but you do have to <u>think it through</u> fairly carefully:

a) <u>SLUGS</u> would <u>increase</u> because there'd be <u>nothing to eat them</u> now.

b) <u>PERCH</u> is a bit trickier. With no frogs the herons will get <u>hungry</u> and so will <u>eat more perch</u> (and minnows and insect larvae), so the perch will in fact <u>decrease</u> in number.

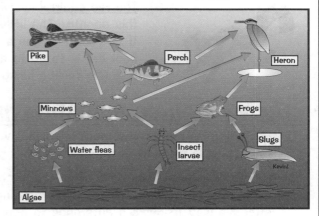

You just have to understand the diagrams (ie. who eats who) and think about it <u>real carefully</u>.

Think about which animals <u>won't now get eaten</u>, and which animals <u>will go hungry</u>, and work out <u>what they'll do about it</u> — and the effect that will have <u>on all the other things</u> in the web.

Don't get bugged by biological pest control...

Biological pest control can take a few months to work. But look on the bright side — it won't take that long to learn. Write yourself a <u>mini-essay</u> on it. Then practise taking animals out of food webs one by one, until you reckon you could do it in your sleep. It's the only way...

Sustainable Development

Sustainable Development is Environmentally Friendly

The Examiners' favourite phrase this year is 'sustainable development'. They've gone potty about it.

> SUSTAINABLE DEVELOPMENT meets the needs of today's population without harming the ability of future generations to meet their own needs.

1) Farming and burning fossil fuels are necessary for our standards of living and there's more demand on them as the population gets bigger.

2) There's only so much abuse our little planet can take. Nowadays, developers can't just build things willy–nilly. They have to take care to sustain the delicate balance on Earth — the gases in the atmosphere and disposal of waste are just a couple of the things they have to look at.

3) Other factors that need to be considered when developing an area are the food and energy resources available, and the impact an increased population will have on the local environment. Most development today must be able to continue into the future with as little impact on the planet as possible.

4) Fishing quotas were introduced to make the fishing industry more sustainable — fish stocks are maintained by stopping people from taking too many fish. And re-plantation of woodland is another attempt to be more environmentally friendly — as old trees are felled, new ones are planted.

5) Since sustainable development is about reducing our impact on the environment, it's good news for endangered species, and can make a real difference to population numbers.

Endangered Species Need Protection

The syllabus mentions these species. They used to be a lot more common in Britain than they are now:

1) The red kite — a bird of prey that was nearly wiped out in Britain. People used to kill kites to stop them eating other animals and birds — but there are only a few pairs left now.

2) The osprey — a bird of prey that lives by lakes and eats fish. They became really rare because of competition from anglers for fish. But the fact that Victorian people kept nicking their eggs didn't help.

3) The red squirrel — when the larger grey squirrel was introduced to this country, the little reds couldn't compete for food or territory. If you want to see a red squirrel in this country nowadays, your best bet is to go to a nature reserve (or the Highlands of Scotland if you're feeling lucky).

There are Three Main Ways to Protect Endangered Species

1) Education — maybe the most important way. Organisations like the RSPB and Greenpeace teach people what to do (and often what not to do) to keep habitats safe.

2) Protected sites — since it's often unfair competition (like with the red squirrel) or the destruction of natural habitat that's causing the problem, maintained habitats are often an effective way to make a difference to population sizes. For the squirrel, this means having wardens to keep competitors out of their little bit of woodland.

3) Legal protection — legislation is sometimes used to stop people from doing even more damage. For example, it's illegal to hunt protected species, or mess around with the land where they live.

I'm endanger of falling asleep to be honest...

Three sections for you here, and they're not too hard really. This year's buzzword seems to be sustainable development, and it'd be a brave person (or a bit of a clot) who ventures into the Exam without a good idea of what it is and why it helps. So learn this stuff, and learn it good.

Revision Summary for Module BD3

There's a lot of words in this section. Most topics are pretty waffly with a lot of drivelly facts, and it can be real hard to learn them all. But learn them you must. You need to practise scribbling down what you can remember on each topic, and then checking back to see what you missed. These questions give you a pretty good idea of what you should know. You need to practise and practise them — till you can float through them all, like a cloud or something.

1) Describe the four main methods of collecting/counting organisms. How do they work?
2) Say what the two limitations of these methods are, and explain them.
3) What are the *eight* basic things which determine the population size of a species?
4) What are the *three* more general factors which determine the size of a population?
5) Sketch a graph of prey and predator populations and explain the shapes.
6) Describe what food chains and food webs are. Give two examples of both.
7) What is the difference between a parasite and a mutualistic relationship? Give an example of a mutualistic relationship.
8) What are number pyramids? Why do you generally get a pyramid of numbers?
9) Why do number pyramids sometimes go wrong, and which pyramids are always right?
10) Where does the energy in a food chain originate? Name three ways in which the energy is lost.
11) Explain how you might improve the efficiency of food production.
12) Which two organisms are responsible for the decay of organic matter?
13) What are the five ideal conditions for making compost? Draw a compost maker.
14) What is the Carbon Cycle all to do with? Draw as much of it from memory as you can.
15) What is the Nitrogen Cycle all about? Draw as much of it from memory as you can.
16) What are the four different types of bacteria involved in the Nitrogen Cycle? Describe in detail what each one does.
17) What is happening to the world's population? What is largely responsible for this trend?
18) What can be said about the birth rate and death rate in developing countries?
19) What problems does a rapidly increasing population create for a country?
20) What effect does the ever-increasing number of people have on the environment?
21) Which gas causes acid rain? Where does this gas come from?
22) What are the three main harmful effects of acid rain?
23) What is the great bonus of modern farming methods? What are the drawbacks?
24) Why are chemical pesticides used? What are the drawbacks of doing this?
25) How do pesticides accumulate in food chains? What happened in the 1960s with DDT?
26) What is the main advantage of biological pest control?
27) What is the main disadvantage of biological pest control?
28) Explain how biological pest control works in glass houses.
29) What is the definition of 'sustainable development'? Why is it desirable?
30) Give three examples of endangered species in Britain.
31) Describe how endangered species are protected.

Chemical Equations

Chemical formulae and equations need a lot of practice if you're going to get them right. They can get real tricky real quickly, unless you really know your stuff. Every time you do an equation you need to practise getting it right rather than skating over it.

Chemical Changes Form New Substances

1) When a chemical change occurs you get new substances from the original ones.

2) For example, when a piece of iron is put into a copper (II) sulphate solution a chemical change takes place and two new substances are formed.

> iron + copper (II) sulphate → iron (II) sulphate + copper

3) A chemical change is a process which cannot easily be reversed.

4) There are often large temperature changes involved when a chemical change occurs.

5) You need to know how to recognise a chemical change. There are three tell-tale signs:

A change in *APPEARANCE*
A change in *MASS*
A change in *TEMPERATURE*

Chemical Formulae Tell You How Many Atoms There Are

1) Hydrogen chloride has the chemical formula HCl. This means that in any molecule of hydrogen chloride there will be: one atom of hydrogen bonded to one atom of chlorine.

2) Ammonia has the formula NH_3. This means that in any molecule of ammonia there will be: three atoms of hydrogen bonded to one atom of nitrogen. Simple.

3) A chemical reaction can be described by the process reactants → products.
  eg. magnesium + oxygen → magnesium oxide
which means magnesium reacts with oxygen to produce magnesium oxide.
You have to know how to write these reactions in both words and symbols, as shown below:

The Symbol Equation shows the atoms on both sides:

Magnesium + Oxygen → Magnesium oxide	Methane + Oxygen → Water + Carbon Dioxide
$2Mg \quad + \quad O_2 \quad → \quad 2MgO$	$CH_4 \quad + \quad 2O_2 \quad → \quad 2H_2O \quad + \quad CO_2$

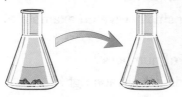

You Need to Know how to Write Out Any Equation...

You really do need to know how to write out chemical equations.
In fact you need to know how to write out equations for pretty well all the reactions in this book.
That might sound like an awful lot, but there aren't nearly as many as you think. Have a look.

Chemical Formulae — it's all elementary...

Make sure you know the formulae for all the compounds you've come across so far.
Try writing symbol equations for the following equations :
  1) Iron(III) oxide + hydrogen → iron + water
  2) Dilute hydrochloric acid + aluminium → aluminium chloride + hydrogen

Balancing Equations

Things start to get a wee bit tricky now. Hang in there and remember... practice makes perfect.

Balancing **The Equation — Match Them Up** One by One

1) There must always be the same number of atoms on both sides, they can't just disappear.
2) You balance the equation by putting numbers in front of the formulae where needed.
   Take this equation for reacting calcium hydroxide with hydrochloric acid:

$$Ca(OH)_2 \ + \ HCl \ \rightarrow \ CaCl_2 + H_2O$$

The formulae are all correct but the numbers of some atoms don't match up on both sides.
You can't change formulae like $Ca(OH)_2$ to $Ca(OH)_3$. You can only put numbers in front of them:

Method: **Balance just** ONE type of atom **at a time**

The more you practise, the quicker you get, but all you do is this:

1) Find an element that doesn't balance and pencil in a number to try and sort it out.
2) See where it gets you. It may create another imbalance but pencil in another number and see where that gets you.
3) Carry on chasing unbalanced elements and it'll sort itself out pretty quickly.

I'll show you. In the equation above you soon notice we're short of H atoms on the right hand side.
1) The only thing you can do about that is make it $2H_2O$ instead of just H_2O:

$$Ca(OH)_2 \ + \ HCl \ \rightarrow \ CaCl_2 + 2H_2O$$

2) But that now causes too many H atoms on the right hand side, so to balance that up you could try putting 2HCl on the left hand side:

$$Ca(OH)_2 \ + \ 2HCl \ \rightarrow \ CaCl_2 + 2H_2O$$

3) And suddenly there it is! Everything balances. And you'll notice the Cl just sorted itself out.

It's Important that you learn these Chemical Formulae

If you're going to balance equations you'd better know the right chemical formulae as well.
The first thing you need to do is learn the table of common substances, positive ions and negative ions.
Then try and follow the two examples. The main thing to remember when trying to find the chemical
formula of a substance like this is that the total charge must always add up to zero. Enjoy!

Example: Find the formula for potassium chloride.

Well, a potassium ion (K^+) has a +1 charge and chloride (Cl^-) has a –1 charge. So the formula is KCl because...

$$\underset{(+1) \ + \ (-1) \ = \ 0}{KCl}$$

Example: Find the formula for zinc nitrate.

A zinc (Zn^{2+}) has a +2 charge and nitrate ion (NO_3^-) has a –1 charge. To get the total charge to be zero we need to have 2 nitrate ions for every zinc ion.
Hence, the formula is:

$$\underset{(+2) \ + \ (-1)\times 2 \ = \ 0}{Zn(NO_3)_2}$$

Common Substances		Positive Ions		Negative Ions	
Water	H_2O	Sodium	Na^+	Chloride	Cl^-
Carbon dioxide	CO_2	Potassium	K^+	Hydroxide	OH^-
Hydrogen	H_2	Calcium	Ca^{2+}	Nitrate	NO_3^-
Oxygen	O_2	Magnesium	Mg^{2+}	Sulphate	SO_4^{2-}
Hydrochloric acid	HCl	Copper	Cu^{2+}	Oxide	O^{2-}
Nitric acid	HNO_3	Iron (II)	Fe^{2+}	Carbonate	CO_3^{2-}
Sulphuric acid	H_2SO_4	Zinc	Zn^{2+}		
Ammonia	NH_3				

This revision lark — it's all a balancing act...

Learning how to balance chemical equations is really important. Unfortunately, the only way to get good at it is to practise, practise, practise. See if you can balance the equation below and name the substances involved:

$$H_2 \ + \ O_2 \ \rightarrow \ H_2O$$

Rates of Reaction

Reactions can go at all sorts of different Rates

1) One of the <u>slowest</u> is the <u>rusting</u> of iron (it's not slow enough though — what about my little MGB).
2) Other slow reactions include <u>chemical weathering</u>, like acid rain damage to limestone buildings.
3) A <u>moderate speed</u> reaction is a <u>metal</u> (like magnesium) reacting with <u>acid</u> to produce a <u>gentle stream of bubbles</u>.
4) A <u>really fast</u> reaction is an <u>explosion</u>, where it's all over in a <u>fraction of a second</u>.
5) A chemical reaction <u>finishes</u> when one of the reactants is used up. Pretty obvious really.

Bang Bang Blast

The Rate of a Reaction Depends on Four Things:

1)	TEMPERATURE
2)	CONCENTRATION	— (or PRESSURE for gases)
3)	SIZE OF PARTICLES	— (or SURFACE AREA)
4)	CATALYST

LEARN THEM!

Catalysts are used to speed up chemical reactions

A **_CATALYST_** is a substance which **_INCREASES_** the speed of a reaction, without being **_CHANGED_** or **_USED UP_** in the reaction.

<u>Example</u>: Ammonia and oxygen react to produce nitrogen monoxide and water.
The metal <u>platinum</u> is a catalyst for this reaction. It causes the rate of the reaction to <u>increase</u>.

Ammonia + Oxygen →(Platinum Catalyst) Nitrogen monoxide + Water

1) Catalysts are used <u>over and over again</u>. They may need <u>cleaning</u> but they <u>don't</u> get <u>used up</u>.
2) Different <u>reactions</u> use different <u>catalysts</u>.
3) You only need a <u>small amount</u> of a catalyst to speed up a reaction with a large amount of reactants.

Learn these Typical Graphs for Rate of Reaction

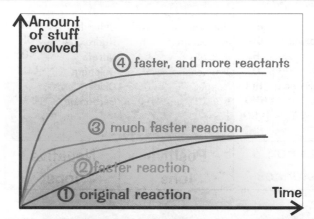

1) <u>Graph 1</u> represents the original <u>fairly slow</u> reaction.
2) <u>Graphs 2 and 3</u> represent the reaction taking place <u>faster</u>, but with the <u>same initial amounts</u>.
3) The <u>increased rate</u> could be due to <u>any</u> of these:

    a) increase in <u>temperature</u>
    b) increase in <u>concentration</u> (or pressure)
    c) solid reactant crushed up into <u>smaller bits</u>
    d) <u>catalyst</u> added.

4) <u>Graph 4</u> produces <u>more product</u> as well as going <u>faster</u>. This can <u>only</u> happen if <u>more reactants</u> are added at the start.

How to get a fast, furious reaction — crack a wee joke...

There's all sorts of bits and bobs of information on this page. To learn it all, you've got to learn to split it up into separate sections and do them one at a time. Practise by <u>covering the page</u> and seeing how much you can <u>scribble down</u> for each section. <u>Then try again, and again</u>...

Collision Theory

Reaction rates are explained perfectly by Collision Theory. It's really simple. It just says that the rate of a reaction simply depends on how often and how hard the reacting particles collide with each other. The basic idea is that particles have to collide in order to react, and they have to collide hard enough as well.

More Collisions increase the Rate of Reaction

All the methods of increasing the rate of reactions can be explained in terms of increasing the number of collisions between the reacting particles:

1) TEMPERATURE increases the number of collisions

When the temperature is increased the particles all move faster. If they're moving more quickly, they're going to have more collisions.

Cold   Hot

2) CONCENTRATION (or PRESSURE) increases the number of collisions

If the solution is made more concentrated it means there are more particles of reactant knocking about between the water molecules which makes collisions between the important particles more likely. In a gas, increasing the pressure means the molecules are more squashed up together so there are going to be more collisions.

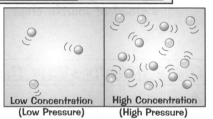
Low Concentration   High Concentration
(Low Pressure)   (High Pressure)

3) SIZE OF SOLID PARTICLES (or SURFACE AREA) increases collisions

If one of the reactants is a solid then breaking it up into smaller pieces will increase its surface area. This means the particles around it in the solution will have more area to work on so there'll be more useful collisions.

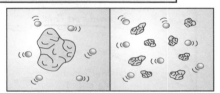

4) CATALYST increases the number of collisions

A catalyst works by giving the reacting particles a surface to stick to where they can bump into each other. This obviously increases the number of collisions too.

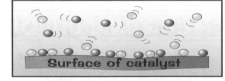
Surface of catalyst

Faster Collisions increase the Rate of Reaction

Higher temperature also increases the energy of the collisions, because it makes the particles move faster.

Faster collisions are ONLY caused by increasing the temperature

Reactions only happen if the particles collide with enough energy. At a higher temperature there will be more particles colliding with enough energy to make the reaction happen. This initial energy is known as the activation energy, and it's needed to break the initial bonds.

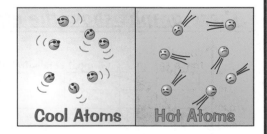
Cool Atoms   Hot Atoms

Collision Theory — All those women/men drivers... (delete as appropriate)

This is quite easy I think. Isn't it all kind of obvious — at least once you've been told it, anyway. The more often particles collide and the harder they hit, the greater the reaction rate. There's a few extra picky details of course (isn't there always!), but you've only got to LEARN them...

Module CD1 — Equations and Rates of Reaction   OCR STAGED ASSESSMENT

Four Experiments on Rate of Reaction

REMEMBER: Any reaction can be used to investigate any of the four factors that affect the rate. This page illustrates two important reactions, but only one factor has been considered for each. But we could just as easily use, say, the marble chips/acid reaction to test the effect of temperature instead.

1) Reaction of Hydrochloric Acid and Marble Chips

This experiment is often used to demonstrate the effect of breaking the solid up into small bits.

1) Measure the volume of gas evolved with a gas syringe and take readings at regular intervals.
2) Make a table of readings and plot them as a graph.
3) Repeat the experiment with exactly the same volume of acid, and exactly the same mass of marble chips, but with the marble more crunched up.
4) Then repeat with the same mass of powdered chalk instead of marble chips.

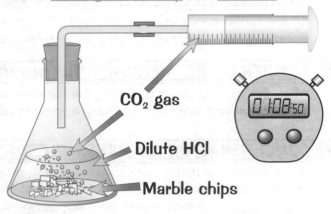

CO₂ gas

Dilute HCl

Marble chips

These graphs show the effect of using finer particles of solid

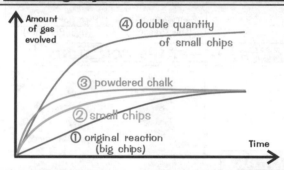

Amount of gas evolved
④ double quantity of small chips
③ powdered chalk
② small chips
① original reaction (big chips)
Time

1) The increase in surface area causes more collisions so the rate of reaction is faster.

2) Graph 4 shows the reaction if a greater mass of small marble chips is added.

3) The extra surface area gives a quicker reaction and there is also more gas evolved overall.

2) Reaction of Magnesium Metal With Dilute HCl

1) This reaction is good for measuring the effects of increased concentration.
2) This reaction gives off hydrogen gas, which we can measure with a mass balance, as shown.
(The other method is to use a gas syringe, as above.)

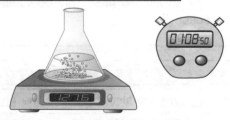

These graphs show the effect of using stronger acid solutions

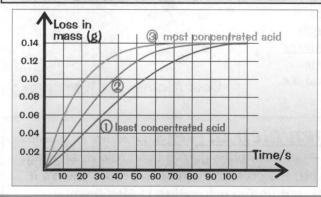

Loss in mass (g)
③ most concentrated acid
②
① least concentrated acid
Time/s
10 20 30 40 50 60 70 80 90 100
0.02 0.04 0.06 0.08 0.10 0.12 0.14

1) Take readings of the mass at regular time intervals.
2) Put the results in a table and work out the loss in mass for each reading. Plot a graph.
3) Repeat with more concentrated acid solutions but always with the same amount of magnesium.
4) The volume of acid must always be kept the same too — only the concentration is increased.
5) The three graphs show the same old pattern. Higher concentration giving a steeper graph with the reaction finishing much more quickly.

Four Experiments on Rate of Reaction

3) Sodium Thiosulphate and HCl produce a Cloudy Precipitate

1) These two chemicals are both <u>clear solutions</u>.
2) They react together to form a <u>yellow precipitate</u> of <u>sulphur</u>.
3) <u>The experiment</u> involves watching a black mark <u>disappear</u> through the <u>cloudy sulphur</u> and <u>timing</u> how long it takes to go.

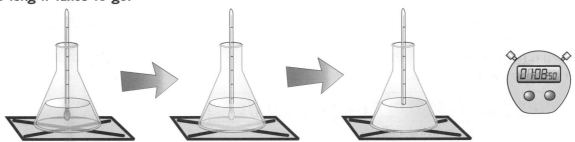

4) The reaction can be <u>repeated</u> for solutions at different <u>temperatures</u>.
5) The <u>depth</u> of liquid must be kept the <u>same</u> each time, of course.
6) The results will of course show that the <u>higher the temperature</u> the <u>quicker the reaction</u> and therefore the <u>less time</u> it takes for the mark to <u>disappear</u>. These are typical results:

Temperature	20°C	25°C	30°C	35°C	40°C
Time taken for mark to disappear	193s	151s	112s	87s	52s

This reaction can <u>also</u> be used to test the effects of <u>concentration</u>.
One sad thing about this reaction is <u>it doesn't give a set of graphs</u>. Well I think it's sad. All you get is a set of <u>readings</u> of how long it took till the mark disappeared for each temperature. Boring.

4) The Decomposition of Hydrogen Peroxide

This is a <u>good</u> reaction for showing the effect of different <u>catalysts</u>.
The decomposition of hydrogen peroxide is:

$$2H_2O_2 \rightleftharpoons 2H_2O + O_2$$

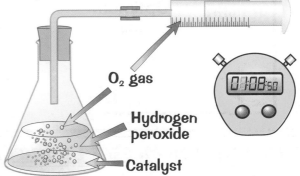

1) This is normally <u>quite slow</u> but a sprinkle of <u>manganese(IV) oxide catalyst</u> speeds it up no end. Other catalysts which work are
   a) <u>potato peel</u> and b) <u>blood</u>.
2) <u>Oxygen gas</u> is given off which provides an <u>ideal way</u> to measure the rate of reaction using the good ol' <u>gas syringe</u> method.

O₂ gas

Hydrogen peroxide

Catalyst

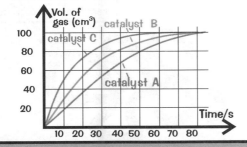

1) Same old graphs of course.
2) <u>Better catalysts</u> give a <u>quicker reaction</u> which is shown by a <u>steeper graph</u> which levels off quickly.
3) This reaction can also be used to measure the effects of <u>temperature</u>, or of <u>concentration</u> of the H_2O_2 solution. The graphs will look <u>just the same</u>.

Four Top Rate Reactions — learn and enjoy

There's always so much happening with reaction rates. Are we looking at products or reactants? Are we measuring gas, or mass, or cloudiness? Is it the effect of temp. or conc. or catalyst or surface area we're investigating? There's so much going on, <u>but you'll just have to sort it out and learn it.</u>

Year 11 Exam · Year 11 Exam · Year 11 Exam · Year 11 Exam · Year 11 Exam

Enzymes

Enzymes crop up in all sorts of places. The eagle-eyed amongst you will no doubt have noticed that enzymes are also mentioned in module BD1 on page 5, which is about digestion.

Enzymes __are__ Biological Catalysts

1) Living things have thousands of different chemical processes going on inside them.
2) The faster these happen the better.
3) Living things also produce enzymes, which act as biological catalysts to speed up all these chemical reactions.
4) Every different biological process has its own enzyme 'designed' especially for it.
5) All enzymes are proteins.

Enzymes __Like it__ Warm __but__ Not Too Hot

1) Chemical reactions in living cells are quite fast in conditions that are warm rather than hot.

2) This is because the cells use enzyme catalysts, which are protein molecules.

3) At low temperatures, a rise in temperature makes the reaction go faster because the particles are moving faster — just like a normal reaction.

4) However, enzymes are usually irreversibly damaged (or denatured) by temperatures above about 45°C, and as the graph shows, their activity drops off sharply when the temperature gets a little too high.

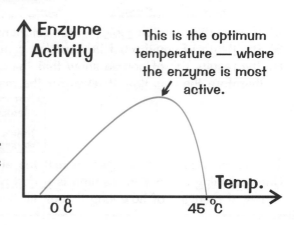

Enzymes __Like it the Right pH__ Too

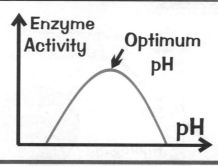

1) The pH affects the activity of enzymes, in a similar way to temperature.

2) The graph shows how the enzyme activity reaches a peak at a certain pH. If the pH is above or below this optimum level, the enzyme activity falls.

3) A pH that's much higher or much lower than the optimum pH causes the enzyme to denature.

4) Different enzymes have different optimum pH levels.

Denaturing __Messes Up the Shape__ of the Enzyme

1) Proteins are very large molecules. They are folded in precise and intricate ways.
2) The part of an enzyme that does the work is called the active site. It holds on to the reactants in the reaction, and 'forces' them to react together.
3) When a protein is denatured by heat or change in pH, the folding gets messed up and its shape changes. When an enzyme is denatured, the shape of its active site changes, which means that it won't work any more.

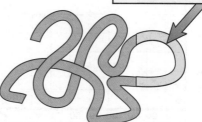

Active site — the reactants bind on here.

"Enzymes" — sounds like a brand of throat lozenge...

This page is definitely a candidate for the mini-essay method. What else is there to say? Scribble down the facts, then look back and see what you missed.

Uses of Enzymes

Living cells use chemical reactions to produce <u>new materials</u>.   Many of these reactions provide products which are <u>useful</u> to us.   Here are <u>three</u> important examples:

Yeast **in Brewing of Beer and Wine:** *Fermentation*

1) <u>Yeast cells</u> convert <u>sugar</u> into <u>carbon dioxide</u> and <u>alcohol</u>.
2) They do this using the <u>enzyme</u> ZYMASE.
3) The main thing is to <u>keep the temperature just right</u>. It has to be between <u>25°C and 55°C</u>.
4) If it's <u>too cold</u> the enzyme won't work very <u>quickly</u>.
5) If it's <u>too hot</u> the yeast dies and the enzymes are <u>denatured</u>.
6) <u>Water</u> needs to be present, simply because yeast is a <u>living organism</u>.
7) It's also important to make sure there is <u>no air</u> present. If there is, then <u>ethanoic acid</u> (or <u>vinegar</u>) is produced instead. Mmmm, tangy.
8) This biological process is called <u>fermentation</u> and is used for making alcoholic drinks like <u>beer and wine</u>.

<u>FERMENTATION</u> is the process of <u>yeast</u> converting <u>sugar</u> into <u>carbon dioxide</u> and <u>alcohol</u>.

$$\text{Glucose} \xrightarrow{\text{Zymase}} \text{Carbon dioxide} \; + \; \text{Ethanol} \quad \text{(+ Energy)}$$

$$C_6H_{12}O_6 \xrightarrow{\text{Zymase}} 2\ CO_2 \; + \; 2\ C_2H_5OH \quad \text{(+ Energy)}$$

Yeast **in Bread-making:** *Fermentation again*

1) The reaction in <u>bread-making</u> is <u>exactly the same</u> as that in <u>brewing</u>.
2) Yeast cells use the enzyme <u>zymase</u> to break down sugar and this gives them <u>energy</u>.
3) It also releases carbon dioxide gas and alcohol as waste products.
4) The <u>carbon dioxide gas</u> is produced <u>throughout</u> the bread mixture and forms in <u>bubbles</u> everywhere.
5) This makes the bread <u>rise</u> and gives it its familiar texture. The small amount of alcohol also gives the bread some extra flavour, no doubt.
6) When the bread is put in the <u>oven</u> the yeast is <u>killed</u> and the <u>reaction stops</u>.

Enzymes are used in *Sweet Production*

1) Most sweets start out as plain old <u>glucose syrup</u>.
2) In the sweet industry, this syrup is produced from <u>starches</u>, using enzymes called <u>amylases</u> (they're found naturally in saliva, where they do the same job).
3) Amylases break down the starch into different sugars, mainly <u>glucose</u> and <u>maltose</u>.
4) These sugars are then <u>processed</u> and have flavours added, to make the sweets you see in shops.

This page is easy — it's a blummin' picnic...

This is rapidly turning into a Domestic Science book. Anyway, you're expected to <u>know</u> all these details of making bread, beer, wine and sweets. <u>Mini-essays, I'd say</u>. Enjoy.

Uses of Enzymes

Yoghurt *and* Cheese *making — only* pasteurised milk

1) Pasteurised milk must be used for making cheese and yoghurt, because fresh unpasteurised milk contains many unwanted bacteria.

2) The pasteurised milk is mixed with specially grown cultures of bacteria.

3) This mixture is kept at the ideal temperature for the bacteria and their enzymes to work.

4) For yoghurt this is pretty warm at about 45°C.

5) The yoghurt-making bacteria convert lactose, (the natural sugar found in milk), into lactic acid. This gives yoghurts their slightly bitter taste.

6) Cheese on the other hand matures better in cooler conditions.

7) Various bacterial enzymes can be used in cheese making to produce different textures and tastes.

Enzymes *are used in* Biological Detergents

1) Enzymes are the 'biological' ingredients in biological detergents and washing powders.

2) They're mainly proteases (protein-digesting enzymes) and lipases (fat-digesting enzymes).

3) Because the enzymes attack animal and plant matter, they're ideal for removing stains like food or blood.

Genetic Engineering *uses Enzymes too*

1) Enzymes are used to "cut" a useful gene from the DNA of say a human.

2) Particular enzymes will cut out particular bits of DNA.

3) Enzymes are then used to cut the DNA of a bacterium, and the human gene is inserted.

4) This "splicing" of a new gene is again controlled by certain specific enzymes.

5) The bacterium now produces some useful product such as human insulin.

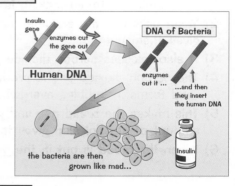

Enzymes *are used to make* Antibiotics

1) Penicillin and other similar antibiotics used to be produced by long, complicated chemical processes. These produced a lot of waste that was damaging to the environment.

2) Today, enzymes are used instead to change the raw penicillin into pure, effective drugs like amoxicillin.

3) In most cases, this process replaces six or seven messy steps with two clean ones.

4) That's good for the environment, and for the drug company — the enzyme method cuts costs and production time dramatically.

Enzymes make cheese nice — that's crackers, surely...

There's really not that much to learn here. Just four sections with a few numbered points in each. Cover the page and write down as much as you can remember. Try another mini-essay.

Revision Summary for Module CD1

This module isn't too bad really. I suppose some of the stuff on Rates of Reaction gets a bit chewy in places, but the rest is all a bit of a breeze really, isn't it? Anyway, here's some more of those nice easy questions which you enjoy so much. Remember, if you can't answer one, look at the appropriate page and learn it. Then go back and try them again. Your hope is that one day you'll be able to glide effortlessly through all of them — it's a nice trick if you can do it.

1) Write down the chemical formulae for the following common substances:
   a) Water   b) Nitric acid   c) Ammonia   d) Sulphuric acid
   e) Hydrogen   f) Oxygen   g) Carbon dioxide   h) Hydrochloric acid

2) Write down the chemical formulae for the following compounds:
   a) Calcium carbonate   b) Iron (II) oxide   c) Zinc chloride
   d) Magnesium sulphate   e) Potassium hydroxide   f) Sodium nitrate

3) Name three things which often accompany a chemical change.

4) What causes a chemical reaction to stop?

5) Give an example of a slow chemical reaction. Now give an example of a fast one.

6) What are the four factors which the rate of reaction depends on?

7) Explain how each of the four factors increases the *number of collisions* between particles.

8) What is the other aspect of collision theory which determines the rate of reaction?

9) Which is the only physical factor which affects this other aspect of the collisions?

10) What happens when hydrochloric acid is added to marble chips?

11) Give details of a possible method for measuring the rate of this reaction.

12) Sketch a typical set of graphs for this method.

13) Describe in detail how you would test the effect on the reaction rate of
   a) finer particles of solid   b) stronger concentration of acid   c) temperature

14) What happens when sodium thiosulphate is added to HCl?
   How is the rate of reaction measured?

15) Write down the equation for the decomposition of hydrogen peroxide.

16) What is the best way to increase the rate of this reaction?

17) What is the best way to measure the rate of this reaction?
   What will the graphs look like?

18) What is the definition of a catalyst?

19) What are enzymes?
   Give three examples of their use in industry.

20) What happens to enzymes if the temperature is above 45°C?

21) Sketch the graph for enzyme activity vs temperature, indicating the temperatures.

22) Give the word-equation for fermentation. Which organism and which enzyme are involved?

23) What temperature range is needed for fermentation to occur?

24) Give the balanced symbol equation for fermentation.

25) What is produced if air is present during fermentation?

26) Explain how enzymes are used in brewing and bread-making.

27) What enzymes are used to produce sugar for the sweet-making industry?

28) What kind of milk is needed for making cheese and yoghurt and why?

29) What gives yoghurt its slightly bitter taste?

30) Explain how biological detergents work.

31) Explain how enzymes are used in genetic engineering and for making antibiotics.

Fractional Distillation

1) <u>Crude oil</u> is formed from the buried remains of plants and animals — it's a fossil fuel. It takes millions of years at high temperature and pressure. We drill down to find crude oil underground.
2) Crude oil is a <u>mixture</u> of <u>hydrocarbons</u> of different sized molecules.
3) <u>Hydrocarbons</u> are basically <u>fuels</u> such as petrol, diesel and LPG (liquefied petroleum gases). They're made of just carbon and hydrogen.
4) The <u>bigger</u> and <u>longer</u> the molecules, the <u>less runny</u> the hydrocarbon (fuel) is.
5) <u>Fractional distillation</u> splits crude oil up into its separate <u>fractions</u>.
6) The <u>shorter</u> the molecules, the <u>lower</u> the <u>temperature</u> at which that fraction <u>condenses</u>.

Crude Oil is Split into Separate Hydrocarbons (fuels)

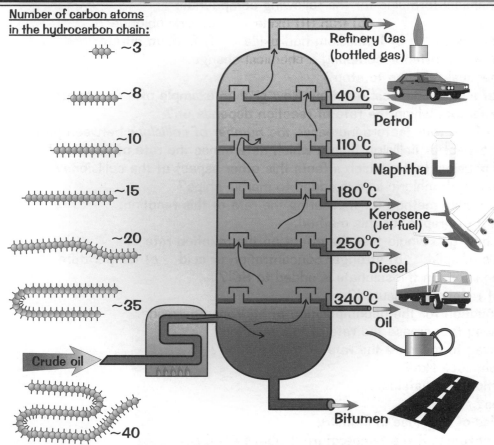

Number of carbon atoms in the hydrocarbon chain:

~3   Refinery Gas (bottled gas)

~8   40°C   Petrol

~10   110°C   Naphtha

~15   180°C   Kerosene (Jet fuel)

~20   250°C   Diesel

~35   340°C   Oil

Crude oil

~40   Bitumen

The <u>temperature gets lower</u> as you go <u>up</u> the <u>fractionating column</u>. That means liquids with <u>lower</u> boiling points will <u>condense higher up</u> in the column.

The <u>fractionating column</u> works continuously, with heated crude oil piped in <u>at the bottom</u> and the various <u>fractions</u> (eg. petrol, diesel, kerosene, LPG etc.) being constantly tapped off at the different levels where they <u>condense</u>.

Long Chain Hydrocarbons Boil/Condense at Higher Temperatures

1) <u>Hydrocarbons</u> are <u>long chain molecules</u>.
2) The <u>intermolecular forces</u> between <u>large</u> hydrocarbon molecules are <u>stronger</u> than those between smaller molecules. During boiling, these intermolecular forces are broken. A long chain molecule needs more energy to break those bonds than a short one. So, as the <u>size</u> of the hydrocarbon molecule increases, the <u>boiling point increases</u>.
3) Condensing is <u>boiling</u> in reverse — things <u>condense</u> at their <u>boiling point</u>.
4) <u>Larger molecules</u> condense near the <u>bottom</u> of the fractionating column. <u>Smaller molecules</u> rise further up the fractionating column (which gets <u>cooler</u> the further up you go) before they reach their boiling point and <u>condense</u> to liquid.

Revising for oil — you know the drill...

A typical question would show a fractionating column and ask you which bit you'd expect petrol or diesel to come out of, so make sure you know <u>all</u> the details. When you think you do, <u>cover up the page</u> and <u>scribble down</u> all the details including the diagram. <u>Then try again</u>.

Higher

Alkanes and Combustion

Crude oil is a mixture of lots of different hydrocarbons — i.e. molecules made out of just <u>hydrogen</u> and <u>carbon</u>. Alkanes are just a particular type of hydrocarbon.

ALKANES have all C–C SINGLE bonds

1) Alkanes are made up of <u>chains</u> of carbon atoms with <u>single</u> covalent bonds between them.
2) They're called <u>saturated</u> hydrocarbons because they have <u>no</u> spare bonds left.
3) The first four alkanes are <u>methane</u> (natural gas), <u>ethane</u>, <u>propane</u> and <u>butane</u>.
4) They're used as fuels. They burn cleanly producing <u>CO_2</u> and <u>water</u>, and releasing lots of <u>heat</u>.

1) Methane
Formula: CH_4

```
    H
    |
H — C — H
    |
    H       (natural
             gas)
```

2) Ethane
Formula: C_2H_6

```
    H   H
    |   |
H — C — C — H
    |   |
    H   H
```

3) Propane
Formula: C_3H_8

```
    H   H   H
    |   |   |
H — C — C — C — H
    |   |   |
    H   H   H
```

4) Butane
Formula: C_4H_{10}

```
    H   H   H   H
    |   |   |   |
H — C — C — C — C — H
    |   |   |   |
    H   H   H   H
```

Complete combustion of Hydrocarbons is safe

During combustion, a substance is combined with oxygen, i.e. it is <u>oxidised</u>.

The <u>complete combustion</u> of any hydrocarbon in oxygen will produce only <u>carbon dioxide</u> and <u>water</u> as waste products, which are both quite <u>clean</u> and <u>non-poisonous</u>.

$$\text{hydrocarbon} + \text{oxygen} \rightarrow \text{carbon dioxide} + \text{water} \quad (+ \text{energy})$$
$$CH_4 + 2O_2 \rightarrow CO_2 + 2H_2O$$

Many <u>gas room heaters</u> release these <u>waste gases</u> into the room, which is perfectly OK. As long as the gas heater is working properly and the room is well ventilated there's no problem. When there's <u>plenty of oxygen</u> the gas burns with a <u>clean blue flame</u>.

But Incomplete combustion of Hydrocarbons is NOT safe

If there <u>isn't enough oxygen</u> the combustion will be <u>incomplete</u>. As well as CO_2 and H_2O, this gives <u>carbon monoxide</u> and <u>carbon</u> as waste products, and produces a <u>smoky yellow flame</u>:

$$\text{hydrocarbon} + \text{oxygen} \rightarrow CO_2 + H_2O + \text{carbon monoxide} + \text{carbon} \quad (+ \text{energy})$$
$$4CH_4 + 6O_2 \rightarrow CO_2 + 8H_2O + 2CO + C$$

The <u>carbon monoxide</u> is a <u>colourless</u>, <u>odourless</u> and <u>poisonous</u> gas and it's <u>very dangerous</u>. Every year people are <u>killed</u> while they sleep, due to <u>faulty</u> gas fires and boilers filling the room with <u>deadly carbon monoxide</u>, CO, and nobody realising. The black carbon given off produces <u>sooty marks</u> and is a <u>clue</u> that the fuel is <u>not</u> burning fully.

The one burning question is... have you learnt it all...

Four features of hydrocarbons which change with increasing chain length, and the details for complete and incomplete combustion. <u>All worth juicy marks in the Exam</u>. So learn and enjoy.

Energy Transfer in Reactions

When chemical reactions occur, <u>energy</u> is usually <u>transferred</u> to or from the <u>surroundings</u>.

In an <u>Exothermic Reaction</u>, Heat is <u>GIVEN OUT</u>

An <u>EXOTHERMIC</u> reaction is one which <u>gives out energy</u> to the surroundings, usually in the form of <u>heat</u> and usually shown by a <u>rise in temperature</u>.

1) The best example of an <u>exothermic</u> reaction is <u>burning fuels</u>. This obviously <u>gives out a lot of heat</u> — it's very exothermic.

2) <u>Neutralisation reactions</u> (acid + alkali) are also exothermic.

3) Another good example is <u>respiration</u>:

Oxygen + Glucose → Carbon Dioxide + Water

4) In an <u>energy level diagram</u> of an exothermic reaction, the <u>difference in height</u> (ΔH) shows energy given out in the reaction.

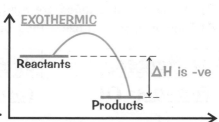

In an <u>Endothermic Reaction</u>, Heat is <u>TAKEN IN</u>

An <u>ENDOTHERMIC</u> reaction is one which <u>takes in energy</u> from the surroundings, usually in the form of <u>heat</u> and usually shown by a <u>fall in temperature</u>.

Endothermic reactions are <u>less common</u> and less easy to spot. <u>LEARN</u> these three examples.

1) <u>Photosynthesis</u> is endothermic — it <u>takes in energy</u> from the sun.

Carbon Dioxide + Water → Oxygen + Glucose
$$6CO_2 + 6H_2O \rightarrow 6O_2 + C_6H_{12}O_6$$

2) <u>Dissolving certain salts in water</u> e.g. 1) potassium chloride 2) ammonium nitrate

3) <u>Thermal decomposition</u>

Heat must be supplied to cause the compound to <u>decompose</u>.
The best example is converting <u>calcium carbonate</u> into <u>quicklime</u> (calcium oxide).

$$CaCO_3 \rightarrow CaO + CO_2$$

In an <u>energy level diagram</u> of an <u>endothermic reaction</u>, the difference in height represents the energy <u>taken in</u> by the reaction. The products are at a <u>higher energy</u> than the reactants. ΔH <u>is positive</u>.

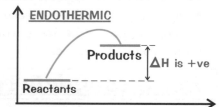

Energy Must Always be <u>Supplied</u> to <u>Break bonds</u>... ...and Energy is Always <u>Released</u> When <u>Bonds Form</u>

1) During a chemical reaction, <u>old bonds</u> are <u>broken</u> and <u>new bonds</u> are <u>formed</u>.

2) Energy must be <u>supplied</u> to break <u>existing bonds</u> — so bond breaking is an <u>endothermic</u> process.

3) Energy is <u>released</u> when new bonds are <u>formed</u> — so bond formation is an <u>exothermic</u> process.

BOND BREAKING - <u>ENDOTHERMIC</u>

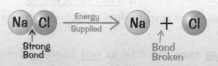

BOND FORMING - <u>EXOTHERMIC</u>

4) In an <u>exothermic</u> reaction, the energy <u>released</u> in bond formation is <u>greater</u> than the energy used in <u>breaking</u> old bonds.

5) In an <u>endothermic</u> reaction, the energy <u>required</u> to break old bonds is <u>greater</u> than the energy <u>released</u> when <u>new bonds</u> are formed.

Measuring Energy Content of Fuels

Different fuels give out <u>different amounts of energy</u> when they burn. One way to measure the energy content of fuels is by using a none-too-fancy copper cup (or a '<u>calorimeter</u>', to give it its proper name).

Use Specific Heat Capacity to Calculate Heat Absorbed

1) This '<u>calorimetric</u>' experiment involves <u>heating water</u> by burning a <u>liquid fuel</u>.

2) If you measure (i) <u>how much fuel</u> you've burned and (ii) <u>how much energy</u> was needed to heat up the water, you can work out how much energy is contained <u>in each gram of fuel</u>.

3) To work out the energy <u>needed to heat up the water</u>, you need to know water's <u>specific heat capacity</u> — this is the <u>amount of energy</u> needed to raise the temperature of <u>1 gram</u> of water by <u>1 °C</u>.

4) The specific heat capacity of <u>water</u> is <u>4.2 J/g/°C</u> — so it takes 4.2 joules of energy to raise the temperature of 1 g of water by 1 °C.

5) If you do the same experiment with <u>different fuels</u>, you can compare their <u>energy content per gram</u>. If a fuel has a <u>higher</u> energy content per gram, you need <u>less fuel</u> to cause the <u>same temperature rise</u>.

Calorimetric Method — Reduce Heat Loss as Much as Possible

1) It's dead important to make as much heat as possible go into <u>heating up</u> the water. <u>Reducing draughts</u> is the key here — use a screen to act as a draught excluder (and don't do it next to an open window).

2) Put some <u>fuel</u> into a <u>spirit burner</u> and <u>weigh</u> the spirit burner <u>full of fuel</u>.

3) Measure out, say, 200 cm³ of water into a <u>copper calorimeter</u>.

4) Take the <u>initial temperature</u> of the water — then put the burner <u>under</u> the calorimeter and <u>light the wick</u>.

5) While the water's heating up, <u>stir</u> it every now and then to distribute the heat <u>evenly</u>.

6) When the heat from the burner has made the water <u>temperature rise</u> by <u>20-30 °C</u>, blow out the spirit burner and make a note of the <u>highest</u> temperature the water reaches.

7) <u>Reweigh</u> the spirit burner and fuel.

Three Calculations to Find the Energy Per Gram of Fuel

1) Use this formula to work out <u>the mass of fuel</u> you've burned:

① MASS OF FUEL BURNED (in g) = INITIAL MASS OF BURNER AND FUEL (in g) − FINAL MASS OF BURNER AND FUEL (in g)

2) The amount of <u>energy absorbed</u> by the water is given by:

② ENERGY ABSORBED (in J) = MASS OF WATER (in g) × SPECIFIC HEAT CAPACITY OF WATER (= 4.2) × TEMPERATURE CHANGE (in °C)

3) Then the <u>energy</u> given out <u>per gram of fuel</u> is given by:

③ ENERGY PRODUCED PER GRAM (in J/g) = $\dfrac{\text{ENERGY SUPPLIED (in J)}}{\text{MASS OF FUEL BURNED (in g)}}$

(This is assuming that <u>all</u> the energy given out by the burning fuel is absorbed by the water.)

Make it a Fair Comparision by Keeping Conditions the Same

1) To <u>compare</u> the energy content of different fuels you need to do the <u>same experiment</u> several times, but using a <u>different fuel</u> in the spirit burner each time.

2) For the comparison to be <u>fair</u>, <u>everything</u> (except the fuel used) should be the <u>same</u>.

3) This means that: (i) you should use the <u>same apparatus</u>,
                 (ii) you should use the <u>same amount of water</u> each time,
                 (iii) the water should <u>start</u> and <u>finish</u> at the <u>same temperature</u> each time.

Hope you've got the energy to revise all this...

The experiment can also be done by using the <u>same amount of fuel</u> in each case, and seeing which causes the <u>largest temperature rise</u>. It's just a different way to do the same thing really.

Fossil Fuels

Fossil Fuels are Used for Heating, Cooking, Transport...

Fossil fuels are pretty varied, and have loads of different uses.
1) Petrol and diesel are used as fuels for cars and lorries.
2) Propane and butane are both used in portable cooking stoves, like the ones you take camping.
3) Paraffin is used as a fuel in heaters. It's also what performers use for fire breathing.
4) Kerosene (what paraffin is called when it's put into planes) is used as a fuel for aircraft.

Various Factors Affect the Choice of Fossil Fuel

Hmm... Some of these may seem obvious but you need to know them thoroughly for the Exam.

1) EASE OF USE

Different fossil fuels are suited to different jobs, and sometimes it's just easier to use one rather than another. For example, it's easier to use natural gas rather than coal to power a domestic oven because you can control the heat more easily. The same goes for Bunsen burners — it's a lot easier to use gas rather than coal.

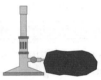

2) POLLUTION

1) Burning any fossil fuel produces CO_2, a greenhouse gas. Fossil fuels also release nitrogen oxides and sulphur dioxide when they burn. These dissolve in water vapour in the air to produce acid rain.
2) If alternative sources of power are available (eg. solar heating in hot countries) they might be preferable.

3) STORAGE

Some fuels require specialist storage facilities, since they're potentially dangerous — gas is an obvious example. These facilities can be expensive to build and maintain.

4) ENERGY VALUE

This is the amount of energy a fuel has the potential to generate. Lignite and anthracite are both types of coal, but anthracite has a much higher energy value, ie. you get more energy from burning a tonne of anthracite than a tonne of lignite.

5) COST

Although lignite has a lower energy value than anthracite, in some countries where both are available, lignite is used in coal-fired power stations because it's easier to mine and therefore cheap.

6) AVAILABILITY

Power stations need good supplies of their raw fuel. This is why coal-fired power stations are sometimes built near coal mines, or have good transport links if they use imported fuel.

7) TOXICITY

Certain toxic compounds are produced when a fossil fuel is burned, and different fuels produce different quantities of these. For example, diesel exhaust fumes contain higher levels of carcinogens (compounds which can cause cancer) than petrol fumes.
Like with pollution, if different forms of energy are available, they might be worth considering.

If fuel excuse me — I've been rather crude...

The bottom line is cost a lot of the time. For example, power stations can be modified so that they are more environmentally friendly, but it's expensive to do. I know what you're thinking — a lot of these seem like common sense. But they still need learning, don't forget.

Evolution of the Atmosphere

The present composition of the atmosphere is: <u>78% nitrogen</u>, <u>21% oxygen</u>, <u>0.035% CO_2</u> (= 99.035%)
The remaining 1% is made up of noble gases (mainly argon). In addition there can be a lot of water vapour.
But the atmosphere wasn't <u>always</u> like this. Here's how the first 4.5 billion years have gone:

Phase 1 — <u>Volcanoes</u> gave out <u>Steam, CO₂</u> and <u>NH₃</u>

1) The Earth's surface was originally <u>molten</u> for many millions of years. Any atmosphere <u>boiled away</u>.
2) Eventually it cooled and a <u>thin crust</u> formed, but <u>volcanoes</u> kept erupting.
3) They belched out mostly <u>carbon dioxide</u>...
4) ...but also some <u>steam</u> and <u>ammonia</u>.
5) The early atmosphere was <u>mostly CO_2</u>.
6) There was virtually <u>no oxygen</u>.
7) The water vapour <u>condensed</u> to form the <u>oceans</u>.
8) <u>Holiday report</u>: Not a nice place to be. Take strong walking boots and a good coat.

Phase 2 — <u>Green Plants Evolved</u> and produced <u>Oxygen</u>

1) <u>Green plants</u> evolved over most of the Earth.
2) They were quite happy in the <u>CO_2 atmosphere</u>.
3) A lot of the early CO_2 <u>dissolved</u> into the oceans.
4) But the <u>green plants</u> steadily <u>removed CO_2</u> and <u>produced O_2</u> by photosynthesis.
5) Much of the CO_2 from the air became <u>locked up</u> in <u>fossil fuels</u> and <u>sedimentary rocks</u>.
6) Ammonia was converted into <u>nitrates</u> by nitrifying bacteria.
7) <u>Nitrogen gas</u> was released by <u>living organisms</u> like denitrifying bacteria.
8) <u>Holiday Report</u>: A bit slimy underfoot. Take wellies and a lot of suncream.

Phase 3 — <u>Ozone Layer</u> allows <u>Evolution</u> of <u>Complex</u> Animals

1) The build-up of <u>oxygen</u> in the atmosphere <u>killed off</u> early organisms that couldn't tolerate it.
2) It also enabled the <u>evolution</u> of more <u>complex</u> organisms that <u>made use</u> of the oxygen.
3) The oxygen also created the <u>ozone layer</u> (O_3), which <u>blocked</u> harmful rays from the sun and <u>enabled</u> even <u>more complex</u> organisms to evolve.
4) There is virtually <u>no CO_2</u> left now.
5) The <u>oceans</u> also contain <u>salts</u> which have been dissolved from <u>rocks</u>. As these salts don't <u>evaporate</u>, the oceans are becoming even saltier.
6) <u>Holiday report</u>: A nice place to be. Get there before the crowds ruin it.

Coo... 4½ Billion Years — just takes your breath away...

I think it's pretty amazing how much the atmosphere has changed. It makes our present day obsession about the CO_2 going up from 0.03% to 0.04% seem a bit ridiculous, doesn't it!
Anyway, never mind that, just <u>learn the three phases with all their details</u>. You don't have to draw the diagrams — although thinking about it, it's a pretty good way to remember it all, don't you think.

Carbon Cycle and the Greenhouse Effect

Examiners like asking questions about the level of carbon dioxide in the atmosphere. <u>So learn it</u>.

The Carbon Cycle Shows how Carbon Changes Form

1) The <u>Carbon Cycle</u> shows how carbon passes through various forms and is constantly <u>recycled</u>.

2) Note that there's only <u>one</u> arrow pointing <u>down</u> in the carbon cycle — representing <u>photosynthesis</u>, which removes CO_2 from the atmosphere.

3) <u>Combustion</u>, plant and animal <u>respiration</u> and <u>decay</u> put CO_2 <u>back into the atmosphere</u>.

4) The different processes largely <u>balance out</u>.

5) This means the proportion of CO_2 in the atmosphere stays <u>pretty much the same</u>.

6) However, the burning of <u>fossil fuels</u> is increasing the level of CO_2 in the atmosphere by releasing carbon which had been locked up for millions of years.

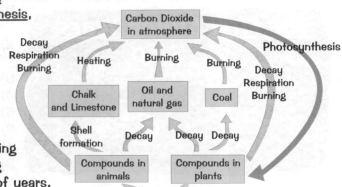

The Greenhouse Effect — CO_2 and Methane Trap Heat from the Sun

1) The <u>temperature</u> of the Earth is a <u>balance</u> between heat it gets from the Sun and heat it radiates back into space.

2) The <u>atmosphere</u> acts like an <u>insulating layer</u> and keeps some of the heat <u>in</u>.

3) This is exactly what happens in a <u>greenhouse</u>. The sun shines in and the glass keeps the <u>heat in</u> — so it gets <u>hotter</u> and <u>hotter</u>.

4) Several different gases in the atmosphere are very good at keeping the heat in. They're called "<u>greenhouse gases</u>" (oddly enough). The main ones we worry about are <u>methane</u> and <u>carbon dioxide</u>.

Modern Industrial Life is Increasing The Greenhouse Effect

1) Mankind has been burning <u>massive amounts</u> of <u>fossil fuels</u> in the last <u>two hundred years</u> or so, which increases the amount of CO_2 going into the atmosphere.

2) The level of CO_2 in the atmosphere has <u>gone up</u> by about <u>20%</u>, and will <u>continue to rise</u> as long as we keep <u>burning fossil fuels</u>.

3) <u>Changes</u> in the atmosphere could lead to changes in <u>weather patterns</u> and <u>climate</u>.

4) Any warming of the Earth could mean the <u>melting</u> of the polar ice-caps, which would <u>raise sea levels</u> and could cause <u>flooding</u> to <u>low-lying coastal parts</u> of the world including many major cities.

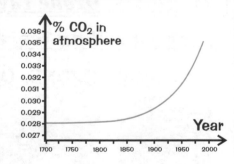

Deforestation increases CO_2 and the Greenhouse Effect

1) Trees unsuitable for timber are <u>burned</u> releasing CO_2 directly into the atmosphere. Microbes also release CO_2 by <u>decaying</u> bits of the felled trees that remain.

2) Because living trees use CO_2 for <u>photosynthesis</u>, removing these trees means that <u>less</u> CO_2 is removed from the atmosphere.

Deforestation — where de train stops in de woods...

Don't be scared of the Carbon Cycle — it's not as bad as it looks. Try making yourself a <u>blank copy</u>. <u>Cover the page</u> and fill in as much as you can remember. Keep going until you know it all.

The Human Effect

The planet's population is increasing dramatically every day — and heating, feeding and clothing all those extra people is putting an ever-increasing strain on the environment.

There's one born every minute — and it's too many

1) The population of the world is currently rising out of control — as the graph shows.

2) This is mostly due to modern medicine, which has stopped widespread death from disease.

3) It's also due to modern farming methods, which can now provide the food needed for so many hungry mouths.

4) More humans means less land for plants and other animals, as well as increased waste.

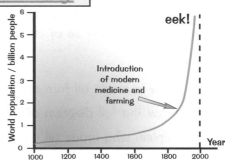

More People means Increased Energy Consumption

As the population increases, the standard of living of people in developed and underdeveloped countries is also increasing. This causes a massive demand for energy.

1) Raw materials, including non-renewable energy resources, are rapidly being used up.

2) Increased use of fossil fuels means more and more waste is being produced.

3) Unless waste is properly handled more pollution will be caused.

Burning Fossil Fuels Causes Acid Rain

1) When fossil fuels are burned they release mostly carbon dioxide which increases the Greenhouse Effect. They also release sulphur dioxide (SO_2). Some fuel remains unburnt and these unburnt hydrocarbons are released into the atmosphere.

2) When SO_2 mixes with clouds it forms sulphuric acid. This then falls as acid rain.

3) Some of the unburnt hydrocarbons are toxic.

4) Cars and power stations are the main sources of these pollutants.

Acid Rain Kills Fish, Trees and Statues

1) Acid rain causes lakes to become acidic, which has a severe effect on its ecosystem. Most plants and animals in lakes just can't survive if the water is too acidic.

2) The way this happens is that the acid causes aluminium salts from soil to dissolve into the water. The resulting aluminium ions are poisonous to fish and birds.

3) Acid rain kills trees.

4) Acid rain damages limestone buildings and ruins stone statues. It's shocking.

Learn about Acid Rain — and always take a coat...

There aren't too many details on acid rain. If you can't learn all this lot properly then you're just not trying. Don't forget they won't ask you easy stuff like "Is acid rain caused by cars or monkeys?", they'll test you on trickier stuff like "Which gases cause acid rain and why?". Learn and enjoy.

Revision Summary for Module CD2

This module is pretty interesting stuff I reckon. Relatively speaking. Anyway, whether it is or it isn't, the only thing that really matters is whether you've learnt it all or not. These questions aren't exactly friendly, but they're a seriously serious way of finding out what you don't know. And don't forget, that's what revision is all about — finding out what you don't know and then learning it till you do. Practise these questions as often as necessary — not just once. Your ultimate aim is to be able to answer all of them easily.

1) How is crude oil formed?

2) Draw the full diagram of fractional distillation of crude oil.

3) Explain why crude oil can be separated by fractional distillation.

4) What are the seven main fractions obtained from crude oil, and what are they used for?

5) What are hydrocarbons? Describe how the boiling point of a hydrocarbon varies with the size of the molecule.

6) Draw the structures of the first four alkanes and give their names.

7) Write balanced equations for the complete and incomplete combustion of a hydrocarbon. Which process is dangerous and why?

8) How can you tell whether or not a hydrocarbon is burning cleanly by the look of the flame?

9) Give the proper definitions of exothermic and endothermic reactions. Give three examples of each.

10) Write word equations and balanced symbol equations for photosynthesis and respiration (the formula for glucose is $C_6H_{12}O_6$)

11) Explain exothermic and endothermic reactions in terms of making and breaking bonds.

12) Describe how a calorimeter is used to measure energy change in a reaction.

13) Give the proper definition of specific heat capacity. Write down the formula that relates energy supplied, mass, SHC and temperature change.

14) What is diesel used for? What is propane used for?

15) Give seven factors that affect the choice of a fossil fuel.

16) What are the percentages of gases in today's atmosphere?

17) What gases did the early atmosphere consist of? Where did these gases come from?

18) What was the main thing which caused phase two of the atmosphere's evolution?

19) Which gas allowed phase three to take place?

20) What is the Carbon Cycle? Draw as much of the diagram from memory as you can.

21) Which gases are increasing the Greenhouse Effect?

22) In what two ways does deforestation add to the Greenhouse Effect?

23) Which gases causes acid rain? Where does they come from?

24) What effects do more and more people have on the environment?

25) What are the three main harmful effects of acid rain?

The Three Different Types of Rock

Rocks shouldn't be confusing. There are <u>three</u> different types: <u>sedimentary</u>, <u>metamorphic</u> and <u>igneous</u>.
Over <u>millions of years</u> they <u>change from one into another</u>. This is called the <u>Rock Cycle</u>. Astonishingly.

The Rock Cycle

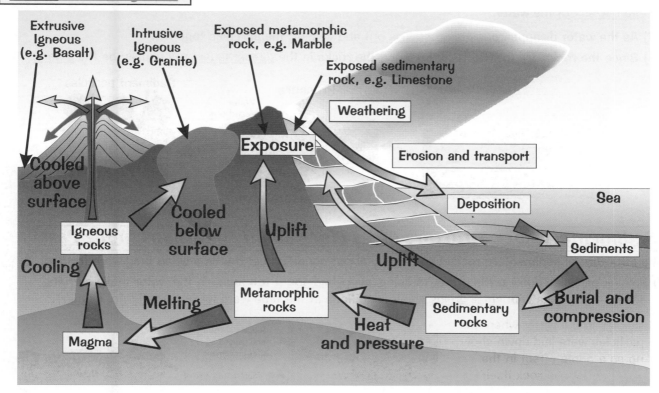

The Rocks Change from One to Another in a Slow Cycle

1) Particles get <u>washed to the sea</u> and settle as <u>sediment</u>.

2) Over <u>millions of years</u> these sediments get <u>crushed</u> into <u>SEDIMENTARY</u> rocks (hence the name).

3) At first they get <u>buried</u>, but they can either <u>rise to the surface</u> again to be discovered, or they can
<u>descend</u> into the <u>heat</u> and <u>pressure</u> below.

4) If they <u>descend</u>, the heat and pressure <u>completely alter</u> the <u>structure</u> of the rock and they then become
<u>METAMORPHIC ROCKS</u> (as in "metamorphosis" or "change". Another good name!).

5) These <u>metamorphic rocks</u> can either <u>rise to the surface</u> to be discovered by an enthusiastic geologist,
or else descend <u>still further</u> into the <u>fiery abyss</u> of the Earth's raging inferno where they will <u>melt</u> and
become <u>magma</u>.

6) When <u>magma</u> reaches the surface it <u>cools</u> and <u>sets</u> and is then called <u>IGNEOUS ROCK</u>.

   ("igneous" as in "ignite" or "fire" — another cool name. Gee, if only biology names were this sensible.)

7) There are actually <u>two types</u> of igneous rock:

   i) <u>EXTRUSIVE</u> — when it comes <u>straight out</u> of the surface from a <u>volcano</u> ("Ex-" as in "Exit").

   ii) <u>INTRUSIVE</u> — when it just sets as a big lump <u>below</u> the surface ("In-" as in "inside").

   (I have to say — whoever invented these names deserves a medal.)

8) When any of these rocks reach the <u>surface</u>, <u>weathering</u> begins and they gradually get <u>worn down</u> and
carried off <u>to the sea</u> and the whole cycle <u>starts over again</u>...   Simple, innit?

Rocks are a mystery — no, no, it's sedimentary my Dear Watson...

Don't you think the Rock Cycle is pretty ace? Can you think of anything you'd rather do than
go on a family holiday to Cornwall, gazing at the cliffs and marvelling at the different types of
rocks and stuff? Exactly. (And even if you can, it's still a good plan to <u>learn about rocks</u>.)

Sedimentary Rocks

Three steps in the Formation of Sedimentary Rocks

1) <u>Sedimentary rocks</u> are formed from <u>layers of sediment</u> laid down in <u>lakes</u> or <u>seas</u>.

2) Over <u>millions of years</u> the layers get <u>buried</u> under more layers, and the <u>weight</u> pressing down <u>squeezes out</u> the water.

3) As the water disappears, <u>salts crystallise out</u> and <u>cement</u> the particles together.

4) Since the rocks are formed layer by layer, the rocks in the <u>deeper layers</u> will usually be the <u>oldest</u>.

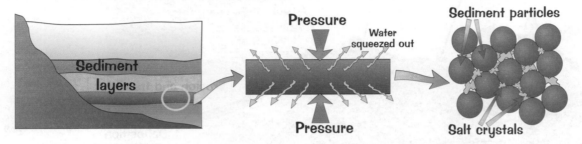

Sedimentary Rock Structure Gives Clues about Conditions in the Past

The structure of sedimentary rocks can tell you about conditions at the time when they were formed.

1) <u>Smaller</u> particles don't settle if they're being <u>swooshed about</u> too much in the water that's carrying them — so rocks with <u>small grains</u> show conditions at the time were <u>less energetic</u> (ie. <u>calmer</u>).

2) <u>Ripples</u> in the <u>water</u> when the particles were laid down show up as a <u>ripple effect</u> in the structure of the rock itself.

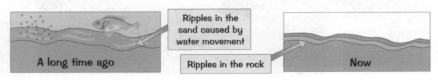

3) <u>Cross bedding</u> is when 'slices' of rock are formed at an angle. Particles are carried by water <u>currents</u> and dropped on a <u>downwards slope</u>. The slope of these <u>cross beds</u> (ie. the slices) shows which direction the current was flowing in at the time.

4) You still get <u>layers</u> of rock stacked up on top of each other (with the older layers nearer the bottom) but each layer is built up from a number of these diagonal <u>cross beds</u>.

Fossils are usually found in Sedimentary Rocks

1) Only <u>sedimentary</u> rocks contain intact fossils. The <u>other two types</u> of rock, metamorphic and igneous, have been through <u>too much heat and trauma</u> to have undamaged fossils left in them.

2) Sedimentary rocks have only been <u>gently crushed</u> for a few million years. No big deal, so the <u>fossils survive</u>. All sedimentary rocks are likely to contain fossils.

3) Fossils are a very useful way of <u>identifying rocks</u> as being of the <u>same age</u>.

4) This is because the fossilised remains that are found <u>change</u> (due to evolution) as the <u>ages pass</u>.

5) This means that if two rocks have the <u>same fossils</u> they must be from the <u>same age</u>.

6) However, if the fossils in two rocks are <u>different</u>, it proves <u>nothing</u> don't forget!

Revision Pressure — don't get crushed by it...

Quite a lot of facts here on sedimentary rocks. You've gotta <u>learn</u> how they <u>form</u>, how to tell if they're <u>older</u>, that they contain <u>fossils</u>, and what you can tell from a rock's <u>structure</u>. It's a good idea to learn the facts, then cover the page and <u>write down</u> what you can remember. Until you know it <u>all</u>.

Metamorphic Rocks

Heat and Pressure Make Metamorphic Rock

Metamorphic rocks are formed by the action of heat and pressure on existing (sedimentary) rocks over many thousands of years.

1) Earth movements can push all types of rock deep underground.

2) Here they are compressed and heated, and the mineral's crystal structure and texture may change.

3) For example, slate (metamorphic) is formed from clay (sedimentary). The heat and pressure make all the tiny particles align in the same direction, giving slate a 'grain'.

4) And the shells that make up limestone are broken down by heat. They then reform as small crystals, forming marble, which has a more even texture and is harder.

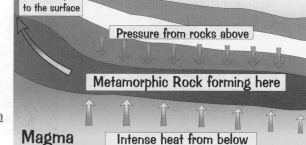

5) Any fossils present in the existing rock are usually distorted or destroyed by the hostile conditions.

6) So long as the rock doesn't actually melt it's classed as metamorphic.

7) If it melts and turns to magma, it's gone. But the magma may resurface as igneous rock.

Different Conditions Give Different Kinds of Metamorphic Rock

1) Sometimes the conditions needed to create metamorphic rocks are caused by the movement of large sections of the Earth's crust — this is known as regional metamorphism.

2) This means you get similar kinds of metamorphic rock over large areas — possibly hundreds of square miles.

3) Metamorphic rocks can also be created when rocks are 'baked' by nearby molten lava (or igneous intrusions — see page 56). This is a more local effect.

4) There are different grades of metamorphic rock depending on the temperatures and pressures that are needed before they'll form. High grade metamorphic rock is formed at high temperatures and pressures. Low grade rock is formed at lower temperatures and pressures.

5) The sedimentary rock mudstone is turned into the intermediate-grade metamorphic rock schist. ('Intermediate-grade' because it's formed at in-between temperatures and pressures.) As the mudstone is heated, new minerals like mica start to form and create layers. These layers of crystals are typical of some kinds of metamorphic rock.

Faults and Folds happen when Rock is Squeezed

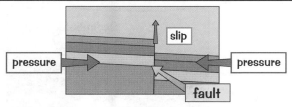

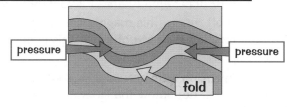

1) Faults form in brittle rock that cracks under pressure.
2) The rock cracks into two pieces — then one piece slips up or down the fault line.
3) Faults can slip gradually or suddenly.

1) Folds form in rock that is bending under pressure.
2) Folds develop very slowly.

Schist! — when the heat and pressure is all too much...

There are quite a lot of details accumulating now, and somehow you've got to make sense of them in your head. If you can draw and label the three diagrams, that's a really good start. But don't let up until you can write down all the fiddly little details from memory. Otherwise it'll get real tricky in the Exam.

Igneous Rocks

1) <u>Igneous rocks</u> form when <u>molten magma</u> pushes up <u>into the crust</u> or <u>right through it</u>.

2) Igneous rocks contain various <u>different minerals</u> in <u>randomly-arranged</u> interlocking <u>crystals</u>.

3) There are <u>two types</u> of igneous rocks: <u>EXTRUSIVE</u> and <u>INTRUSIVE</u>:

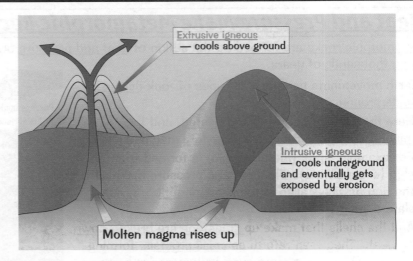

Extrusive igneous — cools above ground

Intrusive igneous — cools underground and eventually gets exposed by erosion

Molten magma rises up

INTRUSIVE igneous rocks cool SLOWLY with BIG crystals
GRANITE is an intrusive igneous rock with big crystals

1) <u>Granite</u> is formed <u>underground</u> where the magma <u>cools down slowly</u>.

2) This means it has <u>big</u> randomly-arranged <u>crystals</u> because it cools down <u>slowly</u>.

3) Granite is a <u>very hard</u> and <u>decorative</u> stone ideal for <u>steps</u> and <u>buildings</u>.

EXTRUSIVE igneous rocks cool QUICKLY with SMALL crystals
BASALT is an extrusive igneous rock with small crystals

1) <u>Basalt</u> is formed <u>on top</u> of the Earth's crust after <u>bursting out</u> of a <u>volcano</u>.

2) This means it has <u>relatively small</u> crystals — because it <u>cooled quickly</u>.

3) If an igneous rock looks '<u>glassy</u>', it's because it cooled down <u>really quickly</u>.

4) Volcanic eruptions also dump tons of <u>ash</u> into the surroundings. This ash sometimes <u>clumps together</u> to form a kind of rock.

Igneous Intrusions Stick Into Surrounding Rock

1) Igneous rock is formed when <u>molten magma</u> cools down.

2) While it's still a bit runny, this magma can seep into any gaps or cracks in the existing rock structure — this is called an <u>igneous intrusion</u>.

3) If an igneous intrusion cuts across a layered pattern of <u>sedimentary rocks</u>, you know the igneous rock must be <u>younger</u> than the sedimentary.

4) The same goes for a <u>crack</u> that cuts across a rock — the crack is definitely <u>younger</u> than the rock itself. That kind of stands to reason really.

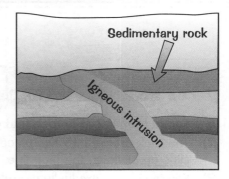

Sedimentary rock

Igneous intrusion

Igneous rocks are real cool — or they're magma...

It's very important that you know what granite looks like. You really should insist that "Teach" organises a field trip to see the famous pink granite coast of Brittany. About two weeks should be enough time to fully appreciate it. In May. Failing that, sit and <u>learn this page</u> in cold grey England for ten minutes.

The Earth's Structure

Brace yourself for a journey to the centre of the Earth...

Crust, Mantle, Outer and Inner Core

1) The crust is very thin (well, about 20km or so!). It's made up of oceanic crust (the bit under the seas) and continental crust (the land)

2) The mantle is liquid, but very viscous. It has a different composition from the crust, and is more dense.

3) The mantle's relatively cold and rigid just below the crust.

4) At greater depths it's hot and not as rigid, and so it's able to flow.

5) The core is just over half the Earth's radius.

6) The core is made from iron and nickel. This is where the Earth's magnetic field comes from.

7) The iron and nickel sank to the "bottom" (ie. the centre of the Earth) long ago because they're denser.

8) The core has a solid inner bit and a liquid outer bit.

9) Radioactive decay creates all the heat inside the Earth.

10) This heat causes the convection currents which cause the plates of the crust to move.

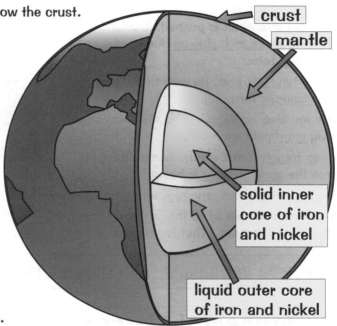

crust
mantle
solid inner core of iron and nickel
liquid outer core of iron and nickel

The Earth's Surface is made up of Large Plates of Rock

1) The Earth's lithosphere consists of the crust and the upper (relatively cool) part of the mantle. It's cracked into pieces called tectonic plates.

2) These plates are like big rafts that float on the rest of the mantle due to their lower density.

3) The map shows the edges of these plates.

4) The plates are moving at a speed of about 1cm or 2cm per year due to convection currents in the mantle below them. As they move, the continents move too.

5) This plate movement produces frequent earthquakes and volcanic activity at the plate boundaries.

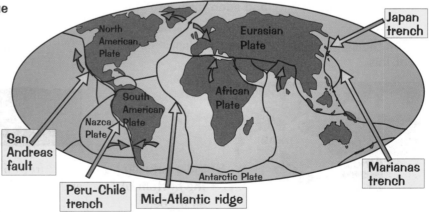

North American Plate
Eurasian Plate
Japan trench
San Andreas fault
South American Plate
Nazca Plate
African Plate
Marianas trench
Peru-Chile trench
Mid-Atlantic ridge
Antarctic Plate

All this crazy plate stuff is driving me mantle...

More nice easy stuff. That means it's nice easy marks in the Exam too. They do put easy stuff in, just so that everyone gets at least some marks. Just make sure you learn all the details. There's nothing dafter than missing easy marks. Cover the page and check you know it all.

Plate Boundaries

At the boundaries between tectonic plates there's usually trouble like volcanoes or earthquakes. There are three different ways that plates interact: colliding, separating or sliding past each other.

Oceanic and Continental Plates Colliding: The Andes

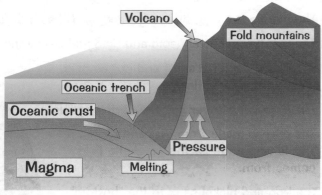

1) The oceanic plate is always forced underneath the continental plate due to its higher density.

2) This is called a subduction zone.

3) As the oceanic crust is pushed down it melts and pressure builds up due to all the melting rock.

4) This molten rock finds its way to the surface and volcanoes form.

5) There are also earthquakes as the two plates slowly grind past each other.

6) A deep trench forms on the ocean floor where the oceanic plate is being forced down.

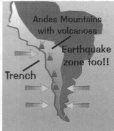

7) The continental crust crumples and folds, forming mountains at the coast.

8) The classic example of all this is the west coast of South America where the Andes mountains are. That region has all the features:

> Volcanoes, earthquakes, an oceanic trench and mountains.

Two Continental Plates Collide: The Himalayas

1) The two continental plates meet head on, neither one being subducted.

2) Any sediment layers lying between the two continent masses get squeezed between them.

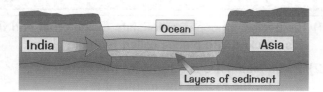

3) These sediment layers inevitably start faulting, crumpling and folding, and soon form into big mountains.

4) The Himalayan mountains are the classic case of this.

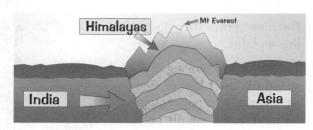

5) India actually broke away from the side of Africa and piled into the bottom of Asia, and is still doing so, pushing the Himalayas up as it goes.

6) Mount Everest is there and is getting higher by a few cm every year as India continues to push up into the continent of Asia.

Another page to learn — don't make a mountain out of it...

Make sure you learn all these diagrams — they summarise all the information in the text. They may well ask you for examples in the Exam, so make sure you know the two different kinds of situation that the Andes and the Himalayas actually represent. Cover and scribble...

Plate Boundaries

Sea Floor Spreading: The Mid-Atlantic Ridge

1) When tectonic plates move apart, magma
rises up to fill the gap and produces new crust made
of the igneous rock basalt (of course).
Sometimes it comes out with great force producing
undersea volcanoes.

2) The Mid-Atlantic ridge runs the whole length
of the Atlantic and actually cuts through the middle
of Iceland, which is why they have
hot underground water.

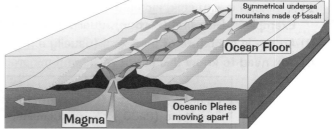

3) As the magma rises up through the gap it forms ridges and
underwater mountains.

4) These form a symmetrical pattern either side of the ridge,
providing strong evidence for the theory of continental drift.

5) However, the most compelling evidence comes from the magnetic
orientation of the rocks.

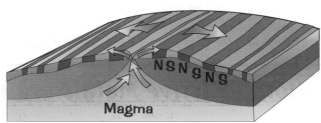

6) As the liquid magma erupts out of the gap, the iron particles in
the rock tend to align themselves with the Earth's magnetic field
and as it cools they set in position.

7) Every half million years or so the Earth's
magnetic field tends to swap direction.

8) This means the rock on either side of the ridge
has bands of alternate magnetic polarity.

9) This pattern is found to be symmetrical either
side of the ridge.

Plates Sliding Past Each Other: San Francisco

1) Sometimes the plates are just sliding past each other.

2) The best known example of this is the San Andreas Fault in California.

3) A narrow strip of the coastline is sliding north at about 7cm a year.

4) Big plates of rock don't glide smoothly past each other.

5) They catch on each other and as the forces build up they suddenly lurch.

6) This sudden lurching only lasts a few seconds — but it'll bring buildings down.

7) The city of San Francisco sits astride this fault line.

8) The city was destroyed by an earthquake in 1906 and hit by another quite
serious one in 1989. They could have another one any time.

The Movement of Plates leads to Deformation of Rocks

1) Movement of tectonic plates can lead to the faulting and folding of rock.

2) The plate movements can also lead to all types of rock being pushed deep underground.

3) Here they are compressed and heated and new metamorphic rocks may be formed.

Learn about Plate Tectonics — but don't get carried away...

Learn the bits of evidence which support the theory that there are big plates of rock moving
about. Learn them well enough to be able to answer a question like this: "Describe the
evidence which supports the theory of Plate Tectonics" (5 marks). Learn, cover, scribble, etc...

Metal Ores From the Ground

Rocks, Minerals and Ores

1) A rock is a mixture of minerals.

2) A mineral is any solid element or compound found naturally in the Earth's crust.
   Examples: Diamond (carbon), quartz (silicon dioxide), bauxite (aluminium oxide).

3) An ore is a mixture of a mineral (usually a metal or a metal compound) and surrounding rock.

4) You need to know this list of rocks and minerals, along with the substances they're converted into.

Rock / Mineral		Converted into...
Clay	→	Pottery
Limestone ($CaCO_3$)	→	Cement
Rock Salt (NaCl)	→	Chlorine and Sodium Hydroxide
Sand (SiO_2)	→	Glass

Metals are Extracted from ores using Carbon or Electrolysis

1) Extracting a metal from its ore involves a chemical reaction to separate the metal out.

2) In many cases the metal is found as an oxide — there are two of these you need to know:

   a) Iron ore is called Haematite, which is iron(III) oxide, formula Fe_2O_3.

   b) Aluminium ore is called Bauxite, which is aluminium oxide, formula Al_2O_3.

3) The TWO common ways of extracting a metal from its ore are:
   a) Chemical reduction using carbon or carbon monoxide,
   b) Electrolysis.

4) Gold and Silver are two of the few metals found as metals rather than in a chemical compound.

More Reactive Metals are Harder to Get

1) The more reactive metals took longer to be discovered (eg. aluminium, sodium).

2) The more reactive metals are also harder to extract from their mineral ores.

3) The above two facts are obviously related. It's obvious when you think about it...

Even primitive folk could find gold easy enough just by scrabbling about in streams, and then melt it into ingots and jewellery and statues of ABBA during their 1857 comeback tour, but coming up with a fully operational electrolysis plant to extract sodium metal from rock salt, complete with plastic yukkas in the foyer, just by paddling about a bit... unlikely.

The Position of Carbon In the Reactivity Series decides it...

1) Metals higher than carbon in the reactivity series have to be extracted using electrolysis.

2) Metals below carbon in the reactivity series can be extracted by reduction using carbon.

3) This is because carbon can only take the oxygen away from metals which are less reactive than carbon itself is.

The Reactivity Series	
Sodium	Na
Calcium	Ca
Magnesium	Mg
Aluminium	Al
CARBON	C
Zinc	Zn
Iron	Fe
Copper	Cu
Gold	Au

Extracted using Electrolysis {

Extracted by reduction using carbon {

Miners — they always have to get their ore in...

This page has four sections with three or four important points in each.
They're all important enough to need learning (except the bit about 1857, etc.).
You need to practise repeating the details from memory. That's the only effective method.

Iron — The Blast Furnace

Iron is a very common element in the Earth's crust, but good iron ores are only found in a few select places around the world, such as Australia, Canada and Millom.
Iron is extracted from haematite, Fe_2O_3, by reduction (ie. removal of oxygen) in a blast furnace.
You really do need to know all these details about what goes on in a blast furnace, including the equations.

The Raw Materials are Iron Ore, Coke and Limestone

1) The iron ore (haematite) contains the iron — which is pretty important.
2) The coke is almost pure carbon. This is for reducing the iron oxide to iron metal.
3) The limestone takes away impurities in the form of slag.

Reducing the Iron Ore to Iron:

1) Hot air is blasted into the furnace making the coke burn much faster than normal and the temperature rises to about 1500°C.
2) The coke burns and produces carbon dioxide:

$$C + O_2 \rightarrow CO_2$$
carbon + oxygen → carbon dioxide

3) The CO_2 then reacts with unburnt coke to form CO:

$$CO_2 + C \rightarrow 2CO$$
carbon dioxide + carbon → carbon monoxide

4) The carbon monoxide then REDUCES the iron ore to iron:

$$3CO + Fe_2O_3 \rightarrow 3CO_2 + 2Fe$$
carbon monoxide + iron(III)oxide → carbon dioxide + iron

The carbon monoxide itself combines with the oxygen in iron oxide to form carbon dioxide. This is OXIDATION.

5) The iron is of course molten at this temperature and it's also very dense so it runs straight to the bottom of the furnace where it's tapped off.

Removing the Impurities:

1) The main impurity is sand (silicon dioxide). This is still solid even at 1500°C and would tend to stay mixed in with the iron. The limestone removes it.

2) The limestone is decomposed by the heat into calcium oxide and CO_2.

$$CaCO_3 \rightarrow CaO + CO_2$$

3) The calcium oxide then reacts with the sand to form calcium silicate or slag which is molten and can be tapped off:

$$CaO + SiO_2 \rightarrow CaSiO_3 \text{ (molten slag)}$$

4) The cooled slag is solid, and is used for:
   1) Road building   2) Fertiliser

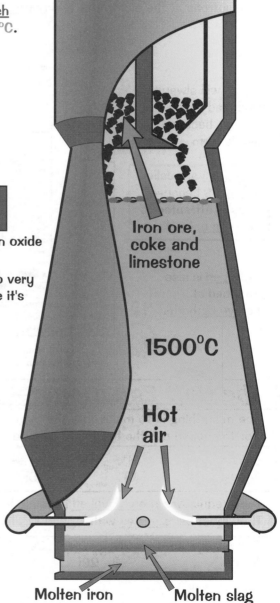

Iron ore, coke and limestone

1500°C

Hot air

Molten iron   Molten slag

Learn the facts about iron extraction — it's a blast...

Three main sections and several numbered points for each. Every bit of it is important and could be tested in the Exam, including the equations. Use the mini-essay method for each section. Alternatively, cover it up one section at a time, and try repeating the facts back to yourself. And keep trying.

Electrolysis and The Half Equations

(Another psychedelic sixties pop group? Sigh... if only.)

Electrolysis _means_ "Splitting Up with Electricity"

1) It requires a liquid, called the electrolyte, which will conduct electricity.

2) Electrolytes are usually free ions dissolved in water,
eg. dilute acids like HCl, and dissolved salts, eg. NaCl solution.

3) Electrolytes can also be molten ionic substances, but this involves higher temperatures. In either case it's the free ions which conduct the electricity and allow the whole thing to work.

4) The electrical supply acts like an electron pump, taking electrons away from the +ve anode and sticking them onto the –ve cathode. Ions gain or lose electrons at the electrodes and neutral atoms and molecules are released.

NaCl dissolved

Molten NaCl

Cathode (-ve) Anode (+ve)

Metals will always be produced at the cathode because metals form +ve ions.

+ve ions are called CATIONS because they're attracted to the –ve cathode.

Hydrogen is also produced at the –ve cathode.

ALL Non-metals (except hydrogen) have –ve ions and so they'll be produced at the +ve anode.

–ve ions are called anions because they're attracted to the anode.

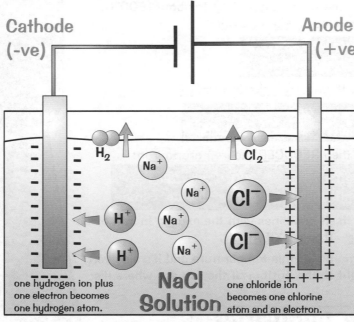

one hydrogen ion plus one electron becomes one hydrogen atom.

NaCl Solution

one chloride ion becomes one chlorine atom and an electron.

In this solution, hydrogen gas forms (from H^+ ions in the water) rather than sodium metal, because sodium is too reactive to form.

The Half Equations — _make sure_ the electrons balance

The main thing is to make sure the number of electrons is the same for both half-equations. For the above cell the basic half equations are:

Cathode: $H^+_{(aq)} + e^- \rightarrow H$
Anode: $Cl^-_{(aq)} \rightarrow Cl + e^-$

These equations aren't finished because both the hydrogen and the chlorine come off as gases. They must be rewritten with H_2 and Cl_2, like this:

Cathode: $2H^+_{(aq)} + 2e^- \rightarrow H_{2(g)}$
Anode: $2Cl^-_{(aq)} \rightarrow Cl_{2(g)} + 2e^-$

Note that there are two electrons in both half equations, which means they're nice and balanced. This gives the overall equation: $2HCl_{(aq)} \rightarrow H_{2(g)} + Cl_{2(g)}$

Cations — sounds like a useful form of pet control...

Practise scribbling down all these details, mini-essay style. Electrolysis can be a bit confusing. I think you have to make an effort to learn all the details, especially how the two half equations are really just one equation, but it kind of happens in two places, joined by a battery.

Extracting Aluminium

A Molten State is needed for Electrolysis

1) Aluminium is more reactive than carbon, so it has to be extracted from its ore by electrolysis.
2) The basic ore is bauxite, and after mining and purifying a white powder is left.
3) This is pure aluminium oxide, Al_2O_3, which has a very high melting point of over 2000°C.
4) For electrolysis to work a molten state is required, and heating to 2000°C would be expensive.

Cryolite is used to Lower the Temperature (and Costs)

1) Instead, the aluminium oxide is dissolved in molten cryolite (a less common ore of aluminium).

2) This brings the temperature needed down to about 900°C, which makes it much cheaper and easier.

3) The electrodes are made of graphite (carbon).

4) The graphite anode (+ve) does need replacing quite often. It keeps reacting to form CO_2.

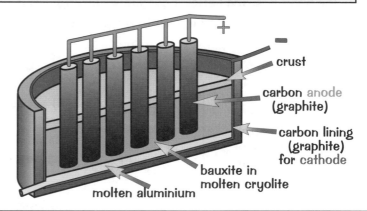

crust

carbon anode (graphite)

carbon lining (graphite) for cathode

bauxite in molten cryolite

molten aluminium

Electrolysis — turning IONS into the ATOMS you want

This is the main object of the exercise:

1) Make the aluminium oxide molten to release the aluminium ions, Al^{3+} so they're free to move.

2) Stick electrodes in — so that the positive Al^{3+} ions will head straight for the negative electrode.

3) At the negative electrode they just can't help picking up some of the spare electrons and 'zup', they've turned into aluminium atoms and they sink to the bottom. Pretty clever, I think.

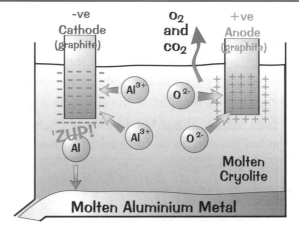

-ve Cathode (graphite)

O_2 and CO_2

+ve Anode (graphite)

Al^{3+} O^{2-}

'ZUP!'

Al^{3+} O^{2-}

Al

Molten Cryolite

Molten Aluminium Metal

Overall, this is a REDOX reaction (REDuction and OXidation) — learn the reactions at both electrodes:

At the Cathode (–ve):

$$Al^{3+} + 3e^- \rightarrow Al$$

(REDUCTION — a gain of electrons)

At the Anode (+ve):

$$2O^{2-} \rightarrow O_2 + 4e^-$$

(OXIDATION — a loss of electrons)

The complete equation for the decomposition of aluminium oxide is then:

$$2Al_2O_3 \rightarrow 4Al + 3O_2$$

Aluminium Oxide   Aluminium   Oxygen

Electrolysis ain't cheap — well, there's always a charge...

Three main sections with several important points to learn for each. Initially you might find it easiest to cover the sections one at a time and try to recall the details in your head. Ultimately though you should aim to repeat it all in one go with the whole page covered.

Purifying Copper by Electrolysis

1) Aluminium is a very reactive metal and has to be removed from its ore by electrolysis.

2) Copper is a very unreactive metal. Not only is it below carbon in the reactivity series, it's also below hydrogen, which means that copper doesn't even react with water.

3) So copper is obtained very easily from its ore by reduction with carbon.

Very Pure Copper is needed for Electrical Conductors

1) The copper produced by reduction isn't pure enough for use in electrical conductors.

2) The purer it is, the better it conducts. Electrolysis is used to obtain very pure copper.

3) This process can also be used to recycle impure copper.

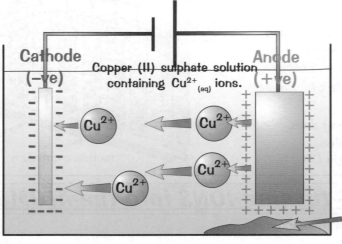

The cathode starts as a thin piece of pure copper and more pure copper adds to it.

The anode is just a big lump of impure copper (sometimes known as boulder) which will dissolve.

The electrical supply acts by:

1) Pulling electrons off copper atoms at the anode causing them to go into solution as Cu^{2+} ions.

2) Then offering electrons at the cathode to nearby Cu^{2+} ions to turn them back into copper atoms.

3) The impurities are dropped at the anode as a sludge, whilst pure copper atoms bond to the cathode.

4) The electrolysis can go on for weeks and the cathode is often twenty times bigger at the end of it.

Pure copper is deposited on the pure cathode (–ve)

Copper dissolves from the impure anode (+ve)

The reaction at the *CATHODE* is:

$$Cu^{2+}_{(aq)} + 2e^- \rightarrow Cu_{(s)}$$

This is an example of reduction. The copper ions have been reduced to copper atoms by gaining electrons.

The reaction at the *ANODE* is:

$$Cu_{(s)} \rightarrow Cu^{2+}_{(aq)} + 2e^-$$

Copper atoms have been oxidised into copper ions by losing electrons. Overall, this is an example of a REDOX reaction. Reduction and oxidation can only occur simultaneously.

Revision and electrolysis — they can both go on for weeks...

This is a pretty easy page to learn. The mini-essay method will do you proud here. Don't forget the diagram and the equations. I know it's not much fun, but think how useful all this chemistry will be in your day-to-day life once you've learned it...

... hmmm, well... learn it anyway.

Atoms

The structure of atoms is real simple. I mean, gee, there's nothing to them. Just learn and enjoy.

The Nucleus

1) It's in the <u>middle</u> of the atom.
2) It contains <u>protons</u> and <u>neutrons</u>.
3) It has a <u>positive charge</u> because of the protons.
4) Almost the <u>whole</u> mass of the atom is <u>concentrated</u> in the nucleus.
5) But size-wise it's <u>tiny</u> compared with the rest of the atom.

The Electrons

1) Move <u>around</u> the nucleus.
2) They're <u>negatively charged</u>.
3) They're <u>tiny</u>, but they cover <u>a lot of space</u>.
4) The <u>volume</u> their orbits occupy determines how big the atom is.
5) They have virtually <u>no</u> mass.
6) They occupy <u>shells</u> around the nucleus.
7) These shells explain <u>the whole of Chemistry</u>.

Number of Protons Equals Number of Electrons

1) Neutral atoms have <u>no charge</u> overall.
2) The <u>charge</u> on the electrons is the <u>same</u> size as the charge on the <u>protons</u> but <u>opposite</u>.
3) This means the <u>number</u> of <u>protons</u> always equals the <u>number</u> of <u>electrons</u> in a <u>neutral atom</u>.
4) If some electrons are <u>added or removed</u>, the atom becomes <u>charged</u> and is then an <u>ion</u>.
5) The number of neutrons isn't fixed but is usually just a bit <u>higher</u> than the number of protons.

Know Your Particles

<u>Protons</u> are <u>Heavy</u> and <u>Positively Charged</u>
<u>Neutrons</u> are <u>Heavy</u> and <u>Neutral</u>
<u>Electrons</u> are <u>Tiny</u> and <u>Negatively Charged</u>

PARTICLE	MASS	CHARGE
Proton	1	+1
Neutron	1	0
Electron	$1/2000$	-1

Simple Ions — Groups 1 & 2 and 6 & 7

1) Remember, atoms that have <u>lost</u> or <u>gained</u> an electron (or electrons) are <u>ions</u>.
2) The elements that most readily form ions are those in Groups 1, 2, 6, and 7.
3) <u>Group 1 and 2 elements</u> are <u>metals</u>, and they <u>lose</u> electrons to form <u>positive ions</u> (called <u>cations</u>, as they're attracted to <u>cathodes</u>). <u>Loss</u> of electrons is called <u>oxidation</u>.
4) <u>Group 6 and 7 elements</u> are <u>non-metals</u>. They <u>gain</u> electrons to form <u>negative ions</u> (called <u>anions</u>, as they're attracted to <u>anodes</u>). <u>Gain</u> of electrons is called <u>reduction</u>.
5) Make sure you know the simple ions in this table:

CATIONS		ANIONS	
Group 1	Group 2	Group 6	Group 7
Li^+	Be^{2+}	O^{2-}	F^-
Na^+	Mg^{2+}		Cl^-
K^+	Ca^{2+}		

6) The <u>noble gases</u> (eg. helium, neon, argon) have a <u>stable number of electrons</u> — their <u>outer</u> electron shell is <u>full</u> (a good thing as far as atoms are concerned). So they don't want to gain or lose any electrons.
7) When <u>other atoms</u> lose or gain electrons, all they're trying to do is get a <u>full outer shell</u> — atom heaven.
8) Elements at <u>opposite sides</u> of the Periodic Table try to get full outer shells by <u>giving</u> and <u>taking</u> electrons — eg. a sodium atom will happily give its single outer-shell electron to a chlorine atom. The chlorine atom gladly takes it because it only needs one more electron to fill its outer shell. Everyone's happy — both atoms' outer shells are now full.

Na^+ → This electron is lost by the sodium atom...

Cl^-

...and gained by the chlorine atom.

Simple ions — looks simple enough to me...

Yet again, more stuff you've <u>got</u> to know. <u>LEARN</u> which atoms form 1+, 1–, 2+ and 2– ions, and why. When you think you've got it, <u>cover the page</u> and start scribbling to see what you really know.

Revision Summary for Module CD3

Module CD3 is pretty interesting stuff I reckon. Relatively speaking. Anyway, whether it is or it isn't, the only thing that really matters is whether you've learnt it all or not. These questions aren't exactly friendly, but they're a seriously serious way of finding out what you don't know. And don't forget, that's what revision is all about — finding out what you don't know and then learning it till you do. Practise these questions as often as necessary — not just once. Your aim is to be able to answer all of them easily.

1) What are the three types of rock? Draw a full diagram of the rock cycle.
2) Explain how the three types of rock change from one to another. How long does this take?
3) Draw diagrams to show how sedimentary rocks form.
4) What are found in sedimentary rocks but are not found in any other type of rock?
5) Draw a diagram to show how metamorphic rocks are formed. What does the name mean?
6) How are igneous rocks formed? What are the two different types?
7) What is the difference in the way that they formed and in their structure and appearance?
8) Draw a diagram of the internal structure of the Earth, with labels.
9) What is the lithosphere?
10) What natural disasters occur at the boundaries between tectonic plates?
11) What happens when an oceanic plate collides with a continental plate? Draw a diagram.
12) What four features does this produce? Which part of the world is the classic case of this?
13) What happens when two continental plates collide? Draw diagrams.
14) What features does this produce? Which part of the world is the classic case of this?
15) What is the Mid-Atlantic ridge? What happens there?
16) Where is the San Andreas fault? What are the tectonic plates doing along this fault line?
17) What are rocks, ores and minerals?
18) What are the common ores of aluminium and iron?
19) Name two metals that are found as metals rather than as ores?
20) What are the two methods for extracting metals from their ores?
21) What decides which method is needed?
22) Draw a diagram of a blast furnace. What are the three raw materials used in it?
23) Write down the equations for how iron is obtained from its ore in the blast furnace.
24) What is slag? Write two equations for the formation of slag, and give two uses of it.
25) How is aluminium extracted from its ore? Give four operational details and draw a diagram.
26) Explain how aluminium metal is obtained from the process, and give the two equations.
27) Explain three reasons why this process is so expensive.
28) How is copper extracted from its ore? How is it then purified, and why does it need to be?
29) Draw a diagram for the purifying process and give the two equations.
30) What is an ion? Give two examples of cations and two examples of anions.
31) What is oxidation? What is reduction?
32) Sketch an atom. Give five details about the nucleus and five details about the electrons.
33) Draw a table showing the relative masses and charges of the three particles found in an atom.
34) Why do atoms want to give away or gain electrons?

Waves — Basic Principles

Waves are <u>different</u> from anything else. They have various features which <u>only</u> waves have:

Amplitude, Wavelength and Frequency

Too many people get these <u>wrong</u>. Take careful note:

1) The <u>AMPLITUDE</u> goes from the <u>middle</u> line to the <u>crest</u>, NOT from a trough to a crest.
2) The <u>WAVELENGTH</u> covers a <u>full cycle</u> of the wave, eg. from <u>crest to crest</u>, not just from *"two bits that are sort of separated a bit"*.
3) <u>FREQUENCY</u> is how many <u>complete waves</u> there are <u>per second</u> (passing a certain point). Frequency is measured in Hertz. 1 Hz is 1 complete wave per second.

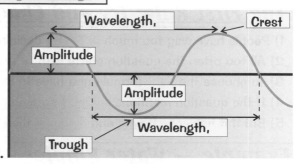

Transverse Waves have Sideways Vibrations

<u>Most waves</u> are <u>transverse</u>:

1) <u>Light</u> and all other <u>electromagnetic radiation</u>.
2) <u>Ripples</u> on water.
3) Waves on <u>strings</u>.
4) A <u>slinky spring</u> wiggled up and down.

In <u>TRANSVERSE WAVES</u> the vibrations are at <u>90⁰</u> to the <u>DIRECTION OF TRAVEL</u> of the wave.

90^0

Vibrations from side to side

Wave travelling this way

Longitudinal Waves have Vibrations along the Same Line

The <u>only longitudinal waves</u> are:

1) <u>Sound</u>. It travels as a longitudinal wave through solids, liquids and gases.
2) <u>Shock waves</u> — eg. seismic <u>P-waves</u>.
3) A <u>slinky spring</u> when plucked.
4) <u>Don't</u> get confused by CRO displays which show a <u>transverse wave</u> when displaying <u>sounds</u>. The real sound wave is <u>longitudinal</u> — the display shows a transverse wave just so you can see <u>what's going on</u>.

In <u>LONGITUDINAL WAVES</u> the vibrations are <u>ALONG THE SAME DIRECTION</u> as the wave is travelling.

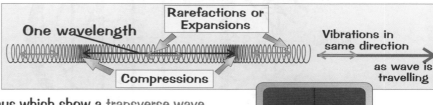

Rarefactions or Expansions

One wavelength

Compressions

Vibrations in same direction as wave is travelling

All Waves Carry Energy — Without Transferring Matter

1) <u>Light</u>, <u>infrared</u>, and <u>microwaves</u> all make things <u>warm up</u>. <u>X-rays</u> and <u>gamma rays</u> can cause <u>ionisation</u> and <u>damage</u> to cells, which also shows that they carry <u>energy</u>.
2) <u>Loud</u> sounds make things <u>vibrate or move</u>.   Even really quiet sounds can move your <u>ear drum</u>.
3) Waves on the sea can <u>toss big boats</u> around and can generate <u>electricity</u>.

Waves can be REFLECTED and REFRACTED and DIFFRACTED

1) They might test whether or not you realise these are <u>properties</u> of waves, so <u>learn them</u>.
2) The three words are confusingly <u>similar</u> but you <u>must</u> learn the <u>differences</u> between them.
3) Light and sound can be <u>reflected</u>, <u>refracted</u> and <u>diffracted</u> and this shows they travel as waves.

Learn about waves — just get into the vibes, man...

This is all very basic stuff on waves. Five sections with some tasty titbits in each. <u>Learn</u> the headings, then the details. Then <u>cover the page</u> and see what you can <u>scribble down</u>. Then try again until you can remember the whole lot. It's all just <u>easy marks to be won</u>... or <u>lost</u>.

Wave Formulae and Reflection

They're just formulae, just like all the other formulae, and the same old rules apply.
But there's more to this page than just boring old formulae. Course there is. Always is.

The First Rule: Try and Choose the Right Formula

1) People have way too much difficulty deciding which formula to use.

2) All too often the question starts with "*A wave is travelling...*", and in they leap with "v = fλ".

3) To choose the right formula you have to look for the three quantities mentioned in the question.

4) If the question mentions speed, frequency and wavelength then sure, "v = fλ" is the one to use.

5) But if it has speed, time and distance then "s = d/t" is more the order of the day — wouldn't you say.

Example — Water Ripples

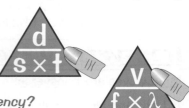

a) *Some ripples travel 55cm in 5 seconds. Find their speed in cm/s.*
   Answer: *Speed, distance and time are mentioned in the question,*
      so you must use "s=d/t": $s = d/t = 55/5 = \underline{11\ cm/s}$

b) *The wavelength of these waves is found to be 2.2cm. What is their frequency?*
   Answer: *This time we have f and λ mentioned, so we use "v = fλ",*
   which tells you that $f = v/\lambda = 11cm/s \div 2.2cm = \underline{5Hz}$ *(It's very cool to use cm/s with cm, s and Hz)*

The Ripple Tank is Really Good for Displaying Waves

Learn all these diagrams showing reflection of waves. They could ask you to complete any one of them in the Exam. It can be quite a bit trickier than you think unless you've practised them real well beforehand.

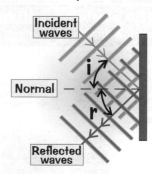

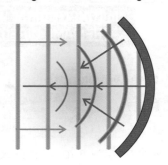

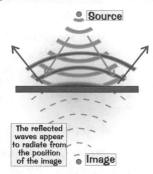

Reflection of Light

1) Reflection of light is what allows us to see objects.

2) When light reflects from an uneven surface such as a piece of paper the light reflects off at all different angles and you get a DIFFUSE REFLECTION.

3) When light reflects from an even surface (smooth and shiny like a mirror) then it's all reflected at the same angle and you get a CLEAR REFLECTION.

4) Sound also reflects off hard surfaces in the form of echoes.

5) Reflection of light and sound gives evidence that light and sound travel as waves.

6) And don't forget, the law of reflection applies to every reflected ray:

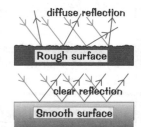

Angle of INCIDENCE = Angle of REFLECTION

Learn reflection thoroughly — try to look at it from all sides...

First make sure you can write down the wave formulae from memory. Then make sure you've learnt the rest well enough to answer typical mean Exam questions like these: "Explain why you can see a piece of paper" "What is a diffuse reflection?" "State the law of reflection."

Refraction: A Property of all Waves

1) <u>Refraction</u> is when waves <u>change direction</u> as they <u>enter a different medium</u>.
2) This is caused <u>entirely</u> by the <u>change in speed</u> of the waves.
3) It also causes the <u>wavelength</u> to change, but remember that the <u>frequency</u> does <u>not</u> change.

1) *Refraction is Shown by Waves in a Ripple Tank Slowing Down*

1) The waves travel <u>slower</u> in <u>shallower water</u>, causing <u>refraction</u> as shown.

2) There's a <u>change in direction</u>, and a <u>change in wavelength</u> but <u>NO change in frequency</u>.

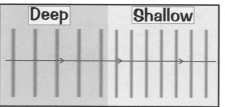
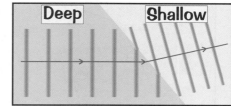

2) *Refraction of Light — The Good Old Glass Block Demo*

You can't fail to remember the old "<u>ray of light through a rectangular glass block</u>" trick.
Make sure you can draw this diagram <u>from memory</u>, with every detail <u>perfect</u>.

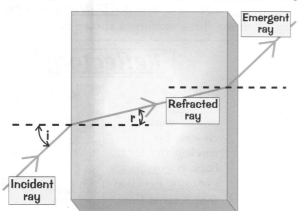

Emergent ray

Refracted ray

Incident ray

1) <u>Take careful note</u> of the positions of the <u>normals</u> and the <u>exact positions</u> of the angles of <u>incidence</u> and <u>refraction</u> (and note it's the angle of <u>refraction</u> — not <u>reflection</u>).

2) Most important of all — remember <u>which way</u> the ray <u>bends</u>.

3) The ray bends <u>towards the normal</u> as it enters the <u>denser medium</u>, and <u>away</u> from the normal as it <u>emerges</u> into the <u>less dense</u> medium.

4) Try to <u>visualise</u> the shape of the <u>wiggle</u> in the diagram — that can be easier than remembering the rule in words.

3) *Refraction Is always Caused By the Waves Changing Speed*

1) When waves <u>slow down</u> they bend <u>towards</u> the normal.

2) When <u>light</u> enters <u>glass</u> it <u>slows down</u> to about <u>2/3</u> of its normal speed (in air) ie. it slows down to about 2×10^8 m/s rather than 3×10^8 m/s.

3) When waves hit the boundary <u>along a normal</u>, ie. at <u>exactly 90°</u>, then there will be <u>no change</u> in direction. That's pretty important to remember, because they often <u>sneak it into a question</u> somewhere. There'll still be a change in <u>speed</u> and <u>wavelength</u>, though.

4) <u>Some</u> light is also <u>reflected</u> when light hits a <u>different medium</u> such as glass.

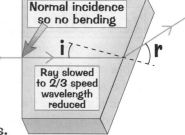

Normal incidence so no bending

Ray slowed to 2/3 speed wavelength reduced

4) *Sound Waves also Refract But it's Hard to Spot*

<u>Sound waves</u> will also refract (change direction) as they enter <u>different media</u>. However, since sound waves are always <u>spreading out so much</u>, the change in direction is <u>hard to spot</u> under normal circumstances. (They bend away from the normal because, unlike light they're speeding up.) But remember, <u>sound waves do refract</u>, OK?

Sound waves

Air

Water

Revise Refraction — but don't let it slow you down...

The first thing you've gotta do is make sure you can spot the difference between the words <u>refraction</u> and <u>reflection</u>. After that you need to <u>learn all this stuff about refraction</u> — so you know exactly what it is. Make sure you know all those <u>diagrams</u> inside out. <u>Cover and scribble</u>.

Total Internal Reflection

Total Internal Reflection and the Critical Angle

1) This only happens when light is coming out of something dense like glass or water or perspex.
2) If the angle is shallow enough the ray won't come out at all, but it reflects back into the glass (or whatever). This is called total internal reflection because all of the light reflects back in.

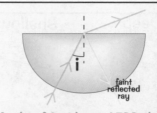

Angle of Incidence LESS than the Critical Angle.
Most of the light passes through into the air but a little bit of it is internally reflected.

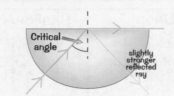

Angle of Incidence EQUAL TO the Critical Angle.
The emerging ray comes out along the surface. There's quite a bit of internal reflection.

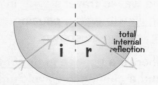

Angle of Incidence GREATER than the Critical Angle.
No light comes out.
It's all internally reflected, ie. total internal reflection.

The Critical Angle for glass is about 42°. This is very handy because it means 45° angles can be used to get total internal reflection, as in the prisms in the three examples shown below.

Binoculars

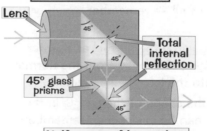

Half a pair of binoculars

Periscope

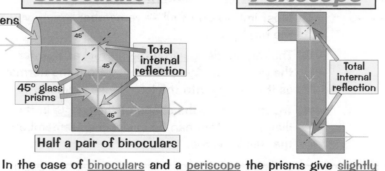

Reflectors

In bicycle reflectors the prisms work cleverly by sending the light back in exactly the opposite direction that it came from.

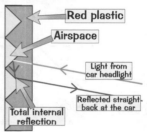

This means that whoever shines the light gets a strong reflection straight back at their eyes.

In the case of binoculars and a periscope the prisms give slightly better reflection than a mirror would, and they're also easier to hold accurately in place. Learn the exact positioning of the prisms.

Optical Fibres — Communications and Endoscopes

1) Optical fibres can carry information over long distances by repeated total internal reflections.
2) The fibre must be narrow enough to keep the angles above the critical angle, as shown, so the fibre mustn't be bent too sharply anywhere.

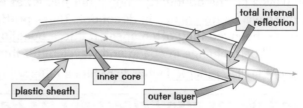

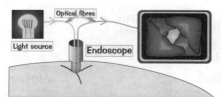

Endoscopes are used to look inside people. It's a narrow bunch of optical fibres with a lens system at each end. Another bunch of fibres carries light down inside to see with. The image is displayed as a full colour moving image on a TV screen. This means they can do operations without cutting big holes in people.

Total Internal Reflection — sounds like a Government Inquiry...

Loads of things to learn here, with diagrams for each. They always have at least one of these applications of total internal reflection in the Exam. Learn them all. None of this is difficult — but just make sure you've got all those little picky details firmly fastened inside your head.

Diffraction

This word sounds a lot more technical than it really is.

Diffraction **is Just the** "Spreading Out" **of Waves**

All waves tend to spread out at the edges when they pass through a gap or past an object. Instead of saying that the wave "spreads out" or "bends" round a corner you should say that it diffracts around the corner. It's as easy as that. That's all diffraction means.

A Wave Spreads More if it Passes Through a Narrow Gap

A ripple tank shows this effect quite nicely. The same effect applies to light and sound too.

 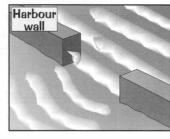

Harbour wall

1) A "narrow" gap is one which is about the same size as the wavelength or less.
2) Obviously then, the question of whether a gap is "narrow" or not depends on the wave in question. What may be a narrow gap for a water wave will be a huge gap for a light wave.
3) It should be obvious then, that the longer the wavelength of a wave, the more it will diffract.

Sounds **Always** Diffract Quite a Lot, **Because** λ **is** Quite Big

1) Most sounds have wavelengths in air of around 0.1m, which is quite long.
2) This means they spread out round corners so you can still hear people even when you can't see them directly (the sound usually reflects off walls too which also helps).
3) Higher frequency sounds will have shorter wavelengths and so they won't diffract as much, which is why things sound more "muffled" when you hear them from round corners.

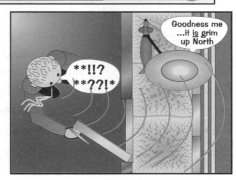

Goodness me ...it is grim up North

**!!? **??!*

Long Wavelength **Radio Waves** Diffract Easily **Over** Hills **and into** Buildings:

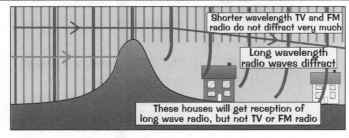

Shorter wavelength TV and FM radio do not diffract very much

Long wavelength radio waves diffract

These houses will get reception of long wave radio, but not TV or FM radio

Visible Light **on the other hand...**

...has a very short wavelength, and it'll only diffract with a very narrow slit:

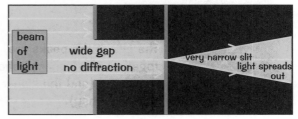

beam of light

wide gap no diffraction

very narrow slit light spreads out

This spreading or diffraction of light (and radio waves) is strong evidence for the wave nature of light.

Diffraction — it can drive you round the bend...

People usually don't know much about diffraction, mainly because there are so few lab demos you can do to show it, and there's also very little to say about it — about one page's worth, in fact. The thing is though, if you just learn this page properly, then you'll know all you need to.

Sound Waves

1) *Sound travels as a Wave:*

Sound can be <u>reflected</u> off walls (echoes), it can be <u>refracted</u> as it passes into different media and it can <u>diffract</u> around doors. These are all standard properties of waves so we deduce that <u>sound travels as a wave</u>. (This "sound" reasoning can also be applied to deduce the <u>wave nature of light</u>.)

2) *Echoes and Reverberation are due to REFLECTED Sound*

1) Sound will only be <u>reflected</u> from <u>hard flat surfaces</u>. Things like <u>carpets</u> and <u>curtains</u> act as <u>absorbing surfaces</u> which will <u>absorb</u> sounds rather than reflect them.

2) This is very noticeable in the <u>reverberation</u> in an <u>empty</u> room. A big empty room sounds <u>completely</u> <u>different</u> once you've put carpet and curtains in, and a bit of furniture, because these things absorb the sound quickly and stop it <u>echoing</u> (reverberating) around the room.

3) *Amplitude is a Measure of the Energy Carried by Any Wave*

1) The greater the <u>amplitude</u>, the more <u>energy</u> the wave carries.

2) In <u>sound</u> this means it'll be <u>louder</u>.

3) <u>Bigger amplitude</u> means a <u>louder sound</u>.

4) With <u>light</u>, a bigger amplitude means it'll be <u>brighter</u>.

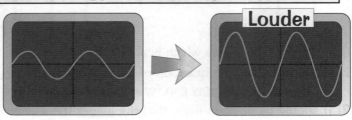

4) *The Frequency of a Sound Wave Determines its Pitch*

1) <u>High frequency</u> sound waves sound <u>high pitched</u> like a <u>squeaking mouse</u>.

2) <u>Low frequency</u> sound waves sound <u>low pitched</u> like a <u>mooing cow</u>.

3) <u>Frequency</u> is the number of complete <u>vibrations</u> each second. It's measured in <u>Hertz</u> (<u>Hz</u>). <u>1 Hertz</u> is one <u>complete</u> vibration per second. Other common units are <u>kHz</u> (1000 Hz) and <u>MHz</u> (1,000,000 Hz).

4) <u>High frequency</u> (or high pitch) also means <u>shorter wavelength</u>.

5) The range of frequencies heard by humans is from 20Hz to 20kHz.

6) These <u>CRO screens</u> are very <u>important</u> so make sure you know all about them:

1) The CRO screens tell us about the <u>pitch</u> and <u>loudness</u> of the sound.

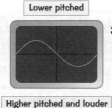

3) When the peaks are <u>further apart</u>, the sound is at a <u>lower pitch</u> (a lower frequency).

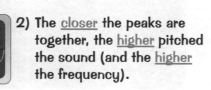

2) The <u>closer</u> the peaks are together, the <u>higher</u> pitched the sound (and the <u>higher</u> the frequency).

4) The CRO screen will show <u>large peaks</u> for a <u>loud</u> noise (sound waves with a <u>big amplitude</u>).

Don't forget that the real sound wave is actually <u>longitudinal</u>, even though the CRO displays a transverse wave.

If sound travelled through vacuum — sunny days would be deafening...

Hmm — not the most interesting page in the world. Still, all those numbered points are <u>important</u> and they're all mentioned specifically in the syllabus. That means you're taking a bit of a chance if you don't learn it pretty darn well. So learning trousers on, and off you go...

Ultrasound

Ultrasound _is Sound with_ a Higher Frequency _than We Can_ Hear

Electrical devices can be made which produce <u>electrical oscillations</u> of <u>any frequency</u>. These can easily be converted into <u>mechanical vibrations</u> to produce <u>sound</u> waves <u>beyond the range of human hearing</u> (ie. frequencies above 20kHz). This is called <u>ultrasound</u> and it has loads of uses:

1) Industrial Cleaning

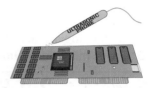

Ultrasound can be used to <u>clean delicate mechanisms</u> without them having to be <u>dismantled</u>. The ultrasound waves can be directed on <u>very precise areas</u> and are extremely effective at <u>removing dirt</u> and other deposits which form on <u>delicate</u> equipment. The alternatives would either <u>damage</u> the equipment or else would require it to be <u>dismantled</u> first.

The same technique is used for <u>cleaning teeth</u>. Dentists use <u>ultrasonic tools</u> to easily and <u>painlessly</u> remove hard deposits of <u>tartar</u> which build up on teeth and which would lead to <u>gum disease</u>.

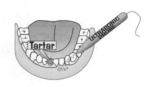

2) Breaking Down Kidney Stones

This works like the cleaning method above. An ultrasound beam concentrates <u>high energy shockwaves</u> at the kidney stone and turns it into <u>sand-like particles</u>. These particles then pass out of the body in <u>urine</u>. It's a good method because the patient <u>doesn't need surgery</u> and it's relatively <u>painless</u>.

3) Industrial Quality Control

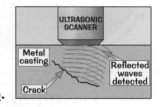

<u>Ultrasound waves</u> can pass through something like a <u>metal casting</u> and whenever they reach a <u>boundary</u> between <u>two different media</u> (like metal and air) some of the wave is <u>reflected back</u> and <u>detected</u>.

The exact <u>timing and distribution</u> of these <u>echoes</u> give <u>detailed information</u> about the <u>internal structure</u>. If there are cracks where there shouldn't be <u>they'll show up</u>.

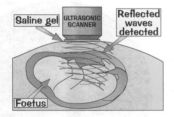

4) For Pre-Natal Scanning of a Foetus

As the ultrasound hits <u>different media</u> some of the sound wave is <u>reflected</u> and these reflected waves are processed by <u>computer</u> to produce a video <u>image</u> of the <u>foetus</u>. No one knows for sure whether ultrasound is safe in all cases but X-rays would definitely be dangerous to the foetus.

5) Range and Direction Finding — SONAR

<u>Bats</u> send out <u>high-pitched squeaks</u> (ultrasound) and pick up the <u>reflections</u> with their <u>big ears</u>. Their brains are able to <u>process</u> the reflected signal and turn it into a <u>picture</u> of what's around.

So the bats basically "<u>see</u>" with <u>sound waves</u>, well enough in fact to <u>catch moths</u> in <u>mid-flight</u> in complete <u>darkness</u> — it's a nice trick if you can do it.

The same technique is used for <u>SONAR</u> which uses <u>sound waves</u> underwater to detect features on the sea-bed. The <u>pattern</u> of the reflections indicates the <u>depth</u> and basic features.

Ultrasound — weren't they a pop group...

Geesh — more sections than you want to know about — but you need to know about them anyway, and I reckon the mini-essay method is going to be a good idea. <u>Learn</u> the five headings, then <u>cover the page</u> and scribble the details down for each, with diagrams. Enjoy.

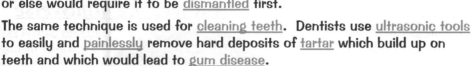

Seismic Waves

Seismic Waves Are Caused By Earthquakes

1) We can only drill about 10km or so into the crust of the Earth, which is not very far, so seismic waves are really the only way of investigating the inner structure.
2) When there's an Earthquake somewhere the shock waves travel out from it and we detect them all over the surface of the planet using seismographs.
3) The time it takes for the two different types of shock wave to reach each seismograph is measured.
4) Seismologists also note the parts of the Earth which don't receive the shock waves at all.
5) From this information you can work out all sorts of stuff about the inside of the Earth as shown below:

S-Waves and P-Waves Take Different Paths

P-Waves are Longitudinal

S-Waves are Transverse

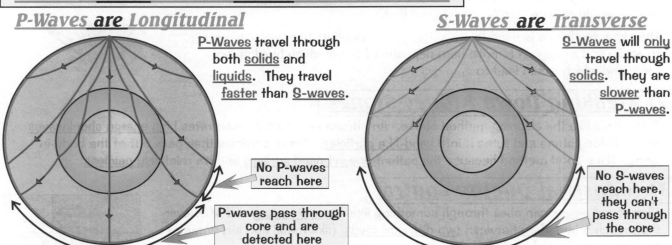

P-Waves travel through both solids and liquids. They travel faster than S-waves.

S-Waves will only travel through solids. They are slower than P-waves.

No P-waves reach here

P-waves pass through core and are detected here

No S-waves reach here, they can't pass through the core

The Seismograph Results Tell Us What's Down There

1) About halfway through the Earth, there's an abrupt change in direction of both types of wave. This indicates that there's a sudden increase in density at that point — the core.
2) The fact that S-waves are not detected in the shadow of this core tells us that it's very liquid.
3) It's also found that P-waves travel slightly faster through the middle of the core, which strongly suggests that there's a solid inner core.
4) Note that S-waves do travel through the mantle, which suggests that it's kinda solid, though I always thought it was made of molten lava which looks pretty liquidy to me when it comes splashing out of volcanoes. Still there you go, just another one of life's little conundrums, I guess.

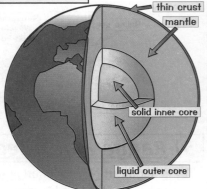

thin crust
mantle
solid inner core
liquid outer core

The Paths Curve Due to Increasing Density (causing Refraction)

1) Both S-waves and P-waves travel faster in more dense material.
2) The curvature of their paths is due to the increasing density of the mantle and core with depth.
3) When the density changes suddenly, the waves change direction abruptly, as shown above.
4) The paths curve because the density of both the mantle and the core increases steadily with increasing depth. The waves gradually change direction because their speed is gradually changing, due to gradual changes in the density of the medium. This is refraction, of course.

Seismic Waves — they reveal the terrible trembling truth...

Once again you've got four main sections to learn. Learn the headings first, then try scribbling down all the details for each heading, including the diagrams. If it helps, remember that S-waves are tranSverSe — so P-waves must be the longitudinal ones. Clever or what.

The Electromagnetic Spectrum

There are Seven Basic Types of Electromagnetic Wave

The properties of electromagnetic waves (EM waves) change as the frequency (or wavelength) changes.
We split them into seven basic types as shown below.
These EM waves form a continuous spectrum so the different regions do actually merge into each other.

RADIO WAVES	MICRO WAVES	INFRA RED	VISIBLE LIGHT	ULTRA VIOLET	X-RAYS	GAMMA RAYS
$1m-10^4$ m	10^{-2} m (3cm)	10^{-5} m (0.01mm)	10^{-7} m	10^{-8} m	10^{-10} m	10^{-12} m

Our eyes can only detect a very narrow range of EM waves, which are the ones we call (visible) light.
All EM waves travel at exactly the same speed as light in a vacuum, and pretty much the same speed as light in other media like glass or water — though this is always slower than their speed in vacuum.

As the Wavelength Changes, So Do The Properties

1) As the wavelength of EM radiation changes, its interaction with matter changes. In particular the way any EM wave is absorbed, reflected or transmitted by any given substance depends entirely on its wavelength — that's the whole point of these three pages of course!
2) As a rule the EM waves at each end of the spectrum tend to be able to pass through material, whilst those nearer the middle are absorbed.
3) Also, the ones at the top end (high frequency, short wavelength) tend to be the most dangerous, whilst those lower down are generally harmless.
4) When any EM radiation is absorbed it can cause two effects:
    a) Heating   b) Creation of a tiny alternating current with the same frequency as the radiation.
5) You need to know all the details that follow about all the different part of the EM spectrum:

Radio Waves are Used Mainly For Communications

1) Radio Waves are used mainly for communication and, perhaps more importantly, for controlling model aeroplanes.
2) Both TV and FM Radio use short wavelength radio waves of about 1m wavelength.
3) To receive these wavelengths you need to be more or less in direct sight of the transmitter, because they will not bend (diffract) over hills or travel very far through buildings.
4) "Long Wave" radio on the other hand has wavelengths of about 1km and these waves will bend over the surface of the Earth and also diffract into tunnels and all sorts.
5) Medium Wave radio signals which have wavelengths of about 300m can be received long distances from the transmitter because they are reflected from the ionosphere, which is an electrically charged layer in the Earth's upper atmosphere. Mind you, these signals are always so fuzzy they're not worth listening to anyway (in my humble opinion).

Medium wave signals reflect off the ionosphere

Ionosphere

FM signals and microwaves must be in line of sight

Long wave signals diffract (bend) around the Earth

The spectrum — isn't that something kinda rude in Biology...

There are lots of details on this page that you definitely need to know. The top diagram is an absolute must — they usually give it you with one or two missing labels to be filled in. Learn the four sections on this page then scribble a mini-essay for each one to see what you know.

Microwaves and Infrared

Microwaves Are Used For Cooking and Satellite Signals

1) Microwaves have two main uses:
cooking food and satellite transmissions.

2) These two applications use two different frequencies of microwaves.

3) Satellite transmissions use a frequency which passes easily through the Earth's atmosphere, including clouds, which seems pretty sensible.

4) The frequency used for cooking, on the other hand, is one which is readily absorbed by water molecules. The microwaves penetrate a few centimetres into the material, before being absorbed by water molecules. The energy is then conducted to more central parts.

5) Microwaves can be dangerous. They can be absorbed by the water molecules in living tissue, which can lead to cells being damaged or killed.

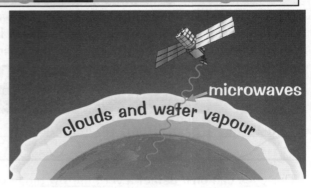

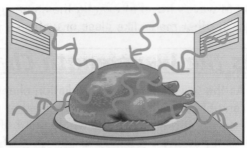

Infrared Radiation — Night-Vision and Remote Controls

1) Infrared (or IR) is otherwise known as heat radiation. This is given out by all hot objects and you feel it on your skin as radiant heat. Infrared is readily absorbed by all materials and causes heating.

2) Radiant heaters (ie. those that glow red) use infrared radiation, including toasters and grills.

3) When used for cooking, IR radiation is absorbed by the surface of the food, and the energy is then conducted to more central parts.

4) Over-exposure to infrared causes damage to cells. This is what causes sunburn.

5) Infrared is also used for night-vision equipment. This works by detecting the heat radiation given off by all objects, even in the dark of night, and turning it into an electrical signal which is displayed on a screen as a clear picture. The hotter an object is, the brighter it appears. Police and the military use this to spot miscreants running away, like you've seen on TV.

6) Infrared is also used for all the remote controls of TVs and videos. It's ideal for sending harmless signals over short distances without interfering with other radio frequencies (like the TV channels).

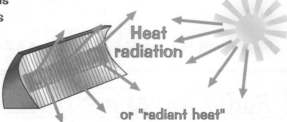

No escape from Infrared — if the Sun doesn't catch you, the Police will...

Each part of the EM spectrum is different, and you definitely need to know all the details about each type of radiation. These are just the kind of things they'll test in your Exams. Do mini essays for microwaves and IR. Then check to see how you did. Then try again... and again...

Visible and UV Light, X-Rays and γ-Rays

Visible light is Used To See With and In Optical Fibres

Visible Light is pretty useful. We use it for seeing with for one thing. You could say that a use of it is in an endoscope for seeing inside a patient's body, but where do you draw the line? — it's also used in microscopes, kaleidoscopes, and pretend telescopes made of old toilet rolls. Seriously though, it is also used in Optical Fibre Digital Communications which is the best one by far for your answer in the Exam.

Ultraviolet Light Causes Skin Cancer

1) This is what causes skin cancer (and also possibly blindness) if you spend too much time in the sun.
2) It also causes your skin to tan. Sunbeds give out UV rays but less harmful ones than the sun does.
3) Darker skin protects against UV rays by preventing them from reaching more vulnerable skin tissues deeper down.
4) There are special coatings which absorb UV light and then give out visible light instead. These are used to coat the inside of fluorescent tubes and lamps.
5) Ultra violet is also useful for hidden security marks which are written in special ink that can only be seen with an ultraviolet light.

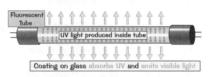

Fluorescent Tube — UV light produced inside tube
Coating on glass absorbs UV and emits visible light

X-Rays Are Used in Hospitals, but are Pretty Dangerous

1) These are used in hospitals to take X-ray photographs of people to see whether they have any broken bones.
2) X-rays pass easily through flesh but not through denser material such as bones or metal.
3) X-rays can cause cancer, so radiographers, who take X-ray pictures all day long wear lead aprons and stand behind a lead screen to keep their exposure to X-rays to a minimum.

Gamma Rays Cause Cancer but Are Used to Treat it Too

1) In high doses, Gamma rays (along with X-rays and UV rays) can kill normal cells.
2) In lower doses all these three types of EM Waves can cause normal cells to become cancerous.
3) If the dose is just right, gamma rays can be used to treat cancer because they kill cancer cells.
4) A big advantage of this treatment is that it avoids surgery.
5) There are disadvantages too. The treatment may damage other normal cells or cause sickness.

The chances of damaging the rest of the body are reduced by taking a few precautions:

Source outside body
-rays focussed on tumour
Source rotated round the outside of the body, with tumour at centre

Gamma Rays are also used in Tracers

1) Doctors can follow the path of a liquid (eg. blood) through the body using a radioactive tracer.
2) A radioactive chemical gets injected or swallowed and is allowed to flow through the body.
3) It's then tracked with a detector outside the body that picks up the radiation.
4) Chemicals used as radioactive tracers have to be chosen carefully.
   Gamma ray sources are used because gamma rays pass out of the body relatively easily, doing little damage on the way. Beta sources (ie. chemicals that emit beta particles) could also be used.

Radiographers are like Teachers — they can see right through you...

Here are the other parts of the EM spectrum for you to learn. Ace, isn't it. At least there's some groovy diagrams to help relieve the tedium. Do a mini-essay for each of the sections, then check, re-learn, re-scribble, re-check, etc. Then put your feet up for a minute or two.

Revision Summary for Module PD1

One thing's for sure — there's quite a few easy facts to learn about waves and radiation. Of course there are still some bits which need thinking about, but really, most of it is fairly easy stuff which just needs learning. Don't forget, this book contains all the important information which they've specifically mentioned in the syllabus, and this is precisely the stuff they're going to test you on in the Exams. You must practise these questions over and over again until they're easy.

1) Sketch a) a transverse wave, b) a longitudinal wave. Give a definition and three examples of each.

2) Define amplitude and wavelength for a wave, and label them on your sketches from Question 1.

3) Give three examples of waves carrying energy.

4) Write down the formula for a wave relating frequency, wavelength and speed.
Write down the formula relating speed, distance and time.

5) Some water ripples travel 60cm in 12 seconds. What is their speed in cm/s?

6) A wave travelling at 20m/s is found to have a wavelength of 5m. What is the frequency?

7) Find the speed of a wave with frequency 50kHz and wavelength 0.3cm.

8) Sketch the patterns when plane ripples reflect at   a) a plane surface,   b) a curved surface.

9) Sketch the reflection of curved ripples at a plane surface.

10) What is the law of reflection? Are sound and light reflected?
Explain why your voice echoes in a tunnel.

11) What is refraction? What causes it? How does it affect wavelength and frequency?

12) Sketch a ray of light going through a rectangular glass block, showing the angles i and r.
What if i=90°?

13) Sketch the three diagrams to illustrate Total Internal Reflection and the Critical Angle.

14) Sketch two applications of total internal reflection which use 45° prisms, and explain them.

15) Give details of two uses of optical fibres. How do optical fibres work?

16) What is diffraction? Sketch the diffraction of   a) water waves,   b) sound waves,   c) light.

17) What's the connection between amplitude and the energy carried by a wave?

18) What's the relationship between frequency and pitch for a sound wave?

19) What is ultrasound? Give full details of five applications of ultrasound.

20) What causes seismic waves? Sketch diagrams showing the paths of both types, and explain.

21) What do seismographs tell us about the structure of the Earth?
Describe the Earth's inner structure.

22) What aspect of EM waves determines their differing properties?

23) Sketch the EM spectrum with all its details. What happens when EM waves are absorbed?

24) Give full details of the uses of radio waves, microwaves and infrared.

25) Detail two uses of X-rays and gamma rays and say how harmful different dosages are.

26) What damage do low doses of gamma radiation cause to body cells?
What effects do higher doses have?

27) Describe in detail how radioactive isotopes are used in each of the following:
a) treating cancer,   b) tracers in medicine.

Heat Transfer

There are <u>three</u> distinct methods of heat transfer: <u>CONDUCTION</u>, <u>CONVECTION</u> and <u>RADIATION</u>.
To answer Exam questions you <u>must</u> use those <u>three key words</u> in just the <u>right places</u>.
And that means you need to know <u>exactly what they are</u>, and all the <u>differences</u> between them.

Heat Energy *Causes* Molecules *to* Move Faster

1) <u>Heat energy</u> causes <u>gas and liquid</u> molecules to move around <u>faster</u>, and causes particles in solids to vibrate <u>more rapidly</u>.

2) When particles move <u>faster</u> it shows up as a <u>rise</u> in temperature.

3) This extra <u>kinetic energy</u> in the particles tends to get <u>dissipated</u> to the <u>surroundings</u>.

4) In other words the <u>heat</u> energy tends to flow <u>away</u> from a hotter object to its <u>cooler</u> surroundings. But then you knew that already. I would hope.

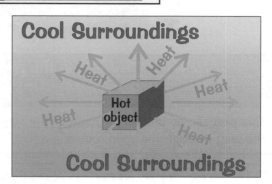

If there's a ***DIFFERENCE IN TEMPERATURE*** between two places then ***HEAT WILL FLOW*** between them.

Conduction, Convection *and* Radiation *Compared*

These differences are really important — so make sure you <u>learn them</u>:

Conduction *and* Convection

1) <u>Conduction</u> occurs mainly in <u>solids</u>.

2) <u>Convection</u> occurs mainly in <u>gases and liquids</u>.

3) Gases and liquids are <u>very poor conductors</u> — convection is usually the <u>dominant</u> process.

Where convection <u>can't</u> occur, the heat transfer by <u>conduction</u> is <u>very slow</u> indeed.

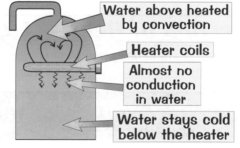

Radiation

1) <u>Radiation</u> travels through anything <u>see-through</u> including a <u>vacuum</u>.

2) <u>Heat Radiation</u> is given out by <u>anything</u> which is <u>warm or hot</u>.

3) The <u>amount</u> of heat radiation which is <u>absorbed or emitted</u> depends on the <u>colour</u> and <u>texture</u> of the <u>surface</u>.

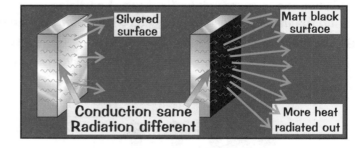

But don't forget, <u>convection</u> and <u>conduction</u> are totally <u>unaffected</u> by surface colour or texture. A <u>shiny white</u> surface <u>conducts</u> just as well as a <u>matt black</u> one.

Learn the facts on heat transfer — but don't get a sweat on...

You've really got to make a fair old effort to get those three key processes of heat transfer all sorted out in your head so that you know exactly what they are and when they occur. There's some more information on the <u>next two pages</u> that might help you get your head round this stuff. So read all three pages before doing your mini-essays. <u>Learn and grin</u>.

Conduction and Convection

Conduction of Heat — Occurs Mainly in Solids

HOT HEAT FLOW **COLD**

> **CONDUCTION OF HEAT** is the process where **VIBRATING PARTICLES** pass on their **EXTRA VIBRATION ENERGY** to **NEIGHBOURING PARTICLES**.

This process continues throughout the solid and gradually the extra vibrational energy (or heat) is passed all the way through the solid, causing a rise in temperature at the other side.

Metals are Much Better Conductors than Non-metals

1) The normal process of conduction, as illustrated above, is very slow. That's why non-metals are such good insulators.

2) Metals, on the other hand, are a totally different ball game. Metals "conduct" well because there are loads of electrons inside the metal that are free to move.

3) The electrons carry the energy through the metal, which is obviously a much faster way of transferring the energy through the metal than slowly passing it between jostling neighbouring atoms.

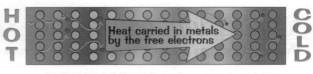

Heat carried in metals by the free electrons

Convection of Heat — Liquids and Gases Only

Gases and liquids are usually free to slosh about — and that allows them to transfer heat by convection, which is a much more effective process than conduction.

> **CONVECTION** occurs when the more energetic particles **MOVE** from the hotter region to the cooler region — **AND TAKE THEIR HEAT ENERGY WITH THEM**.

1) Convection simply can't happen in solids because the particles can't move.

2) When the more energetic (ie. hotter) particles get somewhere cooler they then transfer their energy by the usual process of collisions which warm up the surroundings.

3) The diagram shows a typical convection current. Make sure you learn all the bits about expansion and density changes, which cause the convection current. It's all worth juicy marks in the Exam.

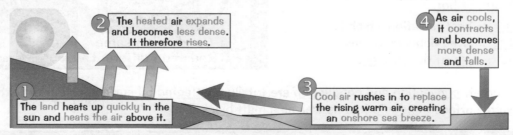

② The heated air expands and becomes less dense. It therefore rises.

④ As air cools, it contracts and becomes more dense and falls.

① The land heats up quickly in the sun and heats the air above it.

③ Cool air rushes in to replace the rising warm air, creating an onshore sea breeze.

Convection Currents — easy as a summer evening breeze...

Oi! Watch out! It's another pair of Physics words that look so much alike that half of you think they're the same word. Look: CONVECTION. See, it's different from CONDUCTION. Tricky that one isn't it. Not just a different word though — convection is a totally different process too. Make sure you learn exactly why it isn't like conduction. Then tell everyone you know.

Heat Radiation

Heat radiation can also be called infrared radiation, and it consists purely of electromagnetic waves of a certain frequency. It's just below visible light in the electromagnetic spectrum.

Heat Radiation Can Travel Through A Vacuum

Heat radiation is different from the other two methods of heat transfer in quite a few ways:

1) It travels in straight lines at the speed of light.
2) It travels through a vacuum. This is the only way that heat can reach us from the Sun.
3) It can be very effectively reflected away again by a silver surface.
4) It only travels through transparent media, like air, glass and water.
5) Its behaviour is strongly dependent on surface colour and texture. This definitely isn't so for conduction and convection.
6) No particles are involved. It's transfer of heat energy purely by waves.

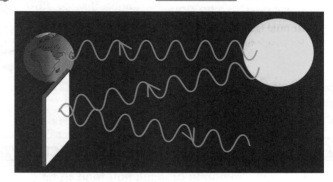

Emission and Absorption of Heat Radiation

1) All objects are continually emitting and absorbing heat radiation.
2) The hotter they are the more heat radiation they emit.
3) Cooler objects around them will absorb this heat radiation. You can feel this heat radiation if you stand near something hot like a fire.

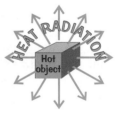

It Depends An Awful Lot on Surface Colour and Texture

1) Dark matt surfaces absorb heat radiation falling on them much more strongly than bright glossy surfaces, such as gloss white or silver. They also emit heat radiation much more too.
2) Silvered surfaces reflect nearly all heat radiation falling on them.
3) In the lab there are several fairly dull experiments to demonstrate the effects of surface on emission and absorption of heat radiation. Here are two of the most gripping:

Leslie's Cube

The matt black side emits most heat so it's that thermometer which gets hottest.

The matt black surface absorbs most heat so its wax melts first and the ball bearing drops.

The Melting Wax Trick

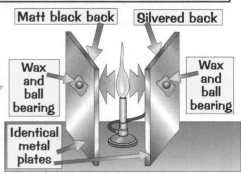

Revise Heat Radiation — absorb as much as you can, anyway...

The main thing to learn here is that heat radiation is strongly affected by the colour and texture of surfaces. Don't forget that the other two types of heat transfer, conduction and convection, are not affected by surface colour and texture at all. Heat radiation is totally different from conduction and convection. Learn all the details on this page, then cover it up and scribble.

Keeping Buildings Warm

Electricity is used to Heat Homes

1) A modern home would be a different place entirely without electricity — no kettles, TVs, lights, videos...
2) And loads of homes are heated using electricity — pretty important too, I reckon.
3) Anything that stops some of this heat escaping is good news — insulation, for example. Such as here...

Loft Insulation
Initial Cost: £200
Annual Saving: £50
Payback time: 4 years

Double Glazing
Initial Cost: £3,000
Annual Saving: £60
Payback time: 50 years

Hot Water Tank Jacket
Initial Cost: £15
Annual Saving: £15
Payback time: 1 year

These figures are in the right ball park, but will vary from house to house.

Cavity Wall Insulation
Initial Cost: £500
Annual Saving: £70
Payback time: 7 years

Draught-proofing
Initial Cost: £50
Annual Saving: £50
Payback time: 1 year

Effectiveness and Cost-effectiveness are not the same...

1) The cheaper methods of insulation tend to be a lot more cost-effective than the pricier ones.
2) The ones that save the most money each year could be considered the most 'effective',
   ie. cavity wall insulation. How cost-effective it is depends on what time-scale you're looking at.
3) If you subtract the annual saving from the initial cost repeatedly then eventually the one with the
   biggest annual saving must always come out as the winner, if you think about it.
4) But you might sell the house (or die) before that happens. If instead you look at it over say, a
   five-year period then the cheap and cheerful draught-proofing wins. Who's to say?
5) But double glazing is always by far the least cost-effective, which is kinda comical, considering.

These Things Trap Air to Prevent Heat Loss

1) Cavity wall insulation — foam in the gaps between the bricks reduces convection and radiation.
2) Loft insulation — a layer of fibre glass wool reduces conduction and radiation through the loft space.
3) Draught proofing — strips of foam and plastic around doors and windows stop draughts of cold air
   blowing in, ie. they reduce heat loss due to convection.
4) Double glazing — two layers of glass with an air gap reduce conduction and radiation.
5) Hot water tank jacket — lagging reduces conduction and radiation from the hot water tank.
6) Thick curtains — these reduce heat loss by conduction and radiation.

Economy 7 Means Cheap Electricity at Night

Economy 7 is a pricing scheme where electricity supplied during the night is cheaper than usual. Storage heaters that heat up at night and then release the heat slowly throughout the day take advantage of this. And if you can leave things like washing machines and dishwashers running at night, then so much the better.

ADVANTAGES of Economy 7
1) Cost-effective for the electricity company — power stations can't be turned off at night, so it's good if there's a demand for electricity at night.
2) Cheaper for consumers if they buy electricity during the off-peak hours.

DISADVANTAGES of Economy 7
1) You start fitting your routine around the cheap rate hours — ie. you might stop enjoying the use of electric during the day.
2) There's a slightly increased risk of fire at night with more appliances going.

They don't seem to have these problems in Spain...

The most effective insulation is the one that keeps the most heat in. If your house had no roof, a roof would be the most effective measure. But cost-effectiveness depends on the time-scale.

Domestic Electricity

Electricity is by far the most <u>useful</u> form of energy. Compared to gas or oil or coal etc. it's <u>much easier</u> to turn it into the <u>four</u> main types of useful energy: <u>heat</u>, <u>light</u>, <u>sound</u> and <u>motion</u>.

Electricity *is a Good* **Power Source in the** Home

<u>ADVANTAGES</u>:
1) Electricity's nice and <u>clean</u>. There's pollution at the <u>production</u> stage, but not at the <u>point of use</u>.
2) It's <u>easy to use</u>. Just plug something into the mains and you're away.
3) Lot's of <u>domestic appliances</u> can be run off the mains — like toasters, videos, tellies etc.
4) You don't have to <u>store</u> electricity in the home, like you'd have to with <u>wood</u> or <u>coal</u>.

<u>DISADVANTAGES</u>:
1) There is always the risk of <u>power cuts</u>.
2) You can get <u>electric shocks</u> from the mains.
3) It's difficult to get mains power out to <u>remote areas</u> — you need <u>very long cables</u>.

Kilowatt-hours *(kW-h) are* 'UNITS' *of* Energy

Your electricity meter counts the number of energy '<u>UNITS</u>' used — otherwise known as <u>kilowatt-hours</u>, or <u>kW-h</u>. A '<u>kW-h</u>' might sound like a unit of power, but it's not — it's an <u>amount of energy</u>.

> A *KILOWATT-HOUR* is the amount of *ELECTRICAL ENERGY*
> used by a *1 KW APPLIANCE* left on for *1 HOUR*.

Make sure you can turn <u>1 kW-h</u> into <u>3,600,000 Joules</u> like this:

"$E = P \times t$" = 1kW × 1 hour = 1000W × 3,600 secs = <u>3,600,000 J</u>   (=3.6 MJ)

(The formula is "Energy = Power×time", and the units must be converted to watts and seconds first.)

The *Two Easy Formulae* **for Calculating The** Cost of Electricity

These must surely be the two most <u>trivial and obvious</u> formulae you'll ever see:

No. of <u>UNITS</u> (kW-h) used = <u>POWER</u> (in kW) × <u>TIME</u> (in hours)	Units = kW × hours

<u>COST</u> = No. of <u>UNITS</u> × <u>PRICE</u> per unit	Cost = Units × Price

<u>EXAMPLE</u>: *Find the cost of leaving a 60 W light bulb on for a) 30 minutes   b) one year.*
<u>ANSWER</u>: a) <u>No. of Units = kW × hours</u> = 0.06kW × ½hr = 0.03 units.
   <u>Cost = Units × price per unit</u> (6.3p)   = 0.03 × 6.3p = <u>0.189p</u> for 30 mins.

   b) <u>No. of Units = kW × hours</u> = 0.06kW × (24×365)hr = 525.6 units.
   <u>Cost = Units × price per unit</u> (6.3p)   = 525.6 × 6.3p = <u>£33.11</u> for one year.

> **N.B.**   Always turn the <u>power</u> into <u>kW</u> (not Watts) and the <u>time</u> into <u>hours</u> (not minutes)

Power Ratings *of Appliances*

Power is the amount of <u>energy</u> used each <u>second</u>. It's measured in <u>watts</u> (W) or <u>kilowatts</u> (kW).

A light bulb converts <u>electrical energy</u> into <u>light</u> and has a power rating of 100W.
A kettle converts <u>electrical energy</u> into <u>heat</u> and has a power rating of 3kW.

The <u>kettle</u> is more <u>expensive</u> to run as its <u>power rating</u> is <u>higher</u>.

Kilowa Towers — *the Best Lit Hotel in Hawaii...*

This page has four sections and you need to learn the stuff in all of them. Start by memorising the headings, then learn the details under each heading. Then <u>cover the page</u> and <u>scribble down</u> what you know. Check back and see what you missed, and then <u>try again</u>. And keep trying.

Year 11 Exam | Year 11 Exam | Year 11 Exam | Year 11 Exam

Year 11 Exam *Year 11 Exam* *Year 11 Exam* *Year 11 Exam* *Year 11 Exam* *Year 11 Exam*

Safety Features

Modern electrical appliances come with built-in safety features.
The main three are <u>fuses</u>, <u>earth wires</u> and <u>circuit breakers</u>.

Plugs and Cables — Learn the Safety Features

There's two reasons for learning this bit, peeps. One, it might be on the exam so it's gonna be handy to know. Two, do it wrong and you could kill yourself. Cheery thoughts all round.

Get the Wiring Right:

1) The <u>right coloured wire</u> to each pin, and <u>firmly screwed</u> in.
2) <u>No bare wires</u> showing inside the plug.
3) <u>Cable grip</u> tightly fastened over the cable <u>outer layer</u>.

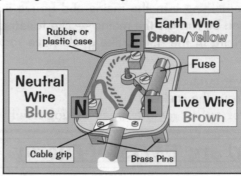

Plug Features:

1) The <u>metal parts</u> are made of copper or brass because these are <u>very good conductors</u>.
2) The case, cable grip and cable insulation are all made of <u>plastic</u> because this is a really good <u>insulator</u>, and is <u>flexible</u> too.
3) This all keeps the electricity flowing <u>where it should</u>.

Earthing and Fuses Prevent Fires and Shocks

The <u>LIVE WIRE</u> alternates between a <u>HIGH +VE AND −VE VOLTAGE</u>, with an average of about <u>230V</u>. The <u>NEUTRAL WIRE</u> is always at <u>0V</u>. Electricity normally flows in and out through the live and neutral wires only. The <u>EARTH WIRE</u> and <u>fuse</u> (or circuit breaker) are just for <u>safety</u>. They work <u>together</u> like <u>this</u>:

1) If a <u>fault</u> develops in which the <u>live</u> somehow touches the <u>metal case</u>, then because the case is <u>earthed</u>, a <u>big current</u> flows in through the <u>live</u>, through the <u>case</u> and out down the <u>earth wire</u>.

2) This <u>surge</u> in current <u>blows the fuse</u> (or trips the circuit breaker), which <u>cuts off</u> the <u>live supply</u>.

3) This <u>isolates</u> the <u>whole appliance</u> making it <u>impossible</u> to get an electric <u>shock</u> from the case. It also prevents the risk of <u>fire</u> caused by the heating effect of a large current — otherwise the flex might overheat for example.

4) <u>Fuses</u> should be <u>rated</u> as near as possible but <u>just higher</u> than the <u>normal operating current</u>.

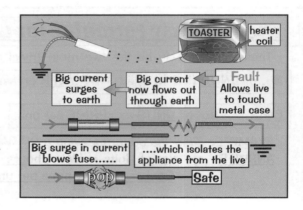

Earthing, Double Insulation and Circuit Breakers — Extra Safety

1) All appliances with <u>metal cases</u> must be "<u>earthed</u>" to avoid the danger of <u>electric shock</u>.
2) "Earthing" just means the metal case must be <u>attached to the earth wire</u> in the cable.
3) If the appliance has a <u>plastic casing</u> and no metal parts <u>showing</u> then it's said to be <u>DOUBLE INSULATED</u>. The plastic case is <u>non-conducting</u>, so it can't become live.
   Anything with <u>double insulation</u> like that <u>doesn't need an earth wire</u>, just a live and neutral.
4) <u>Circuit breakers</u> are basically re-settable fuses. After a problem, you just press a <u>button</u> and everything works again, without having to replace a burned-out wire.

Some people are so careless with electricity — it's shocking...

Make sure you know all the details for wiring a plug and learn what all the different bits of it do. Trickiest of all, make sure you understand how earthing and fuses act together to make things safe. Learnt it all? Good-O. So <u>cover the page</u> and <u>scribble it all down again</u>.

Revision Summary for Module PD2

Another module finished, another page of revision questions to get your teeth sunk into. Have a go at these questions and see how you get on — try them all first, then go back and check over the stuff you can't remember. Practise until you can answer them all without looking back at all. I'll say it again — practise until you can answer them all without looking back at all. When the Exam comes around you won't even break sweat.

1) What causes heat to flow from one place to another?
   What do molecules do as they heat up?

2) Explain briefly the difference between conduction, convection and radiation.

3) Give a strict definition of conduction of heat and say which materials are good conductors.

4) Give a strict definition of convection. Give an example of natural convection.

5) List five properties of heat radiation.

6) Which kind of objects emit and absorb heat radiation?

7) Which surfaces absorb heat radiation best? Which surfaces emit it best?

8) Describe two experiments to demonstrate the effect of different surfaces on radiant heat.

9) List five important ways of insulating houses and say which are the most <u>effective</u> and which are the most <u>cost-effective</u> measures. How do you decide on cost-effectiveness?

10) Describe insulation measures in the home which reduce
    a) conduction,   b) convection,   c) radiation.

11) Which types of heat transfer are insulated against in
    a) double glazing,   b) draught proofing.

12) Describe what is meant by Economy 7 electricity.

13) List three advantages and three disadvantages of using electricity as a power source in the home.

14) What's a kilowatt-hour? Write down the two easy formulae for finding the cost of electricity?

15) How many units of electricity (in kWh) would a kettle of power 3000W use in 2 minutes? How much would that cost, if one unit of electricity costs 8p?

16) Work out the cost of running a light bulb with a power rating of 100W for a full day, if one unit of electricity costs 8p.

17) Sketch a properly wired plug.

18) Why are the metal parts of a plug made from copper or brass?
    Why are the case, cable grip and cable insulation made from plastic?

19) Explain fully how earthing and fuses work.

20) What does it mean if an appliance is 'double-insulated'?

21) What is the advantage of using a circuit breaker as opposed to a normal fuse?

Velocity and Acceleration

Speed and Velocity are Both just: HOW FAST YOU'RE GOING

Speed and velocity are both measured in <u>metres per second</u> — <u>m/s</u> (or km/h or mph). They both simply say <u>how fast</u> you're going, but there's a <u>subtle difference</u> between them which you <u>need</u> to know:

> <u>SPEED</u> is just <u>how fast</u> you're going (eg. 30mph or 20m/s) with no regard to the direction.
> <u>VELOCITY</u> however must <u>also</u> have the <u>DIRECTION</u> specified, eg. 30mph north or 20m/s, 060°.

Seems kinda fussy I know, but they expect you to remember that distinction, so there you go.

Speed, Distance and Time — the Formula:

$$\text{Speed} = \frac{\text{Distance}}{\text{Time}}$$

A lot of the time we tend to use the words "speed" and "velocity" interchangeably. For example, to calculate velocity you'd just use the above formula for speed.

> <u>EXAMPLE</u>: A cat skulks 20m in 35s. Find a) its speed   b) how long it takes to skulk 75m.
> <u>ANSWER</u>: *Using the formula triangle: a) s = d/t = 20/35 = 0.57m/s b) t = d/s = 75/0.57 = 131s*

Acceleration is How Quickly You're Speeding Up

Acceleration is definitely <u>not</u> the same as <u>velocity</u> or <u>speed</u>. When you read or write the word <u>acceleration</u>, remind yourself: "<u>acceleration</u> is <u>completely different</u> from <u>velocity</u>. Acceleration is how <u>quickly</u> the velocity is <u>changing</u>." Velocity is a simple idea — acceleration is more <u>subtle</u>, which is why it's confusing.

Acceleration — The Formula:

$$\text{Acceleration} = \frac{\text{Change in Velocity}}{\text{Time Taken}}$$

Well, it's <u>just another formula</u>. Mind you, there are <u>two tricky things</u> with this one. First there's the "ΔV", which means working out the "<u>change in velocity</u>", as shown in the example below, rather than just putting a <u>simple value</u> for speed or velocity in. Secondly there's the <u>units</u> of acceleration, which are m/s². <u>Not m/s</u>, which is <u>velocity</u>, but m/s². Got it? No?   Let's try once more: <u>Not m/s</u>, but <u>m/s²</u>.

> <u>EXAMPLE</u>: A skulking cat accelerates from 2m/s to 6m/s in 5.6s. Find its acceleration.
> <u>ANSWER</u>: *Using the formula triangle:*   *a = ΔV/t = (6 – 2) / 5.6 = 4 ÷ 5.6 = <u>0.71 m/s²</u>*

Ticker Timers let you Calculate Speed

Two (not exactly space-age) devices for measuring distance and speed are given in the syllabus...

Trundle wheel — this is a <u>wheel</u> (on a stick) that you push along. Some have a '<u>distance-meter</u>' on them. Others <u>click</u> every time the wheel turns a full circle, and you can work out the distance travelled by counting the <u>number of clicks</u> and multiplying by the <u>wheel's circumference</u>.

Ticker timer — you attach a piece of '<u>ticker tape</u>' to a mouse or something, which then pulls the tape through the <u>ticker timer</u>. The timer makes a mark, say, <u>50 times a second</u>.

Ticker tape   Ticker timer

> Each gap represents 1/50 of a second.
> So these 10 gaps represent 1/5 (=0.2) of a second.
>
> |← 10 cm →|
>
> So speed = $\frac{\text{distance}}{\text{time}} = \frac{0.1}{0.2} = 0.5$ m/s

The <u>length of tape</u> between two (far apart) dots is the <u>distance travelled</u> — and the time taken is the <u>number of spaces</u> between your two dots, multiplied by $\frac{1}{50}$ second for each one.

Velocity and Acceleration — learn the difference...

It's true — some people don't realise that velocity and acceleration are <u>totally different things</u>. Hard to believe I know — all part of the great mystery and tragedy of life I suppose.

Year 11 Exam   Year 11 Exam   Year 11 Exam   Year 11 Exam   Year 11 Exam

D-T and V-T Graphs

Make sure you learn all these details real good. Make sure you can distinguish between the two, too.

Distance-Time Graphs

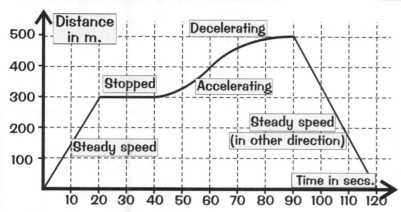

Very Important Notes:

1) Gradient = speed.
2) Flat sections are where it's stopped.
3) The steeper the graph, the faster it's going.
4) Downhill sections mean it's coming back toward its starting point.
5) Curves represent acceleration or deceleration.
6) A steepening curve means it's speeding up (increasing gradient).
7) A levelling off curve means it's slowing down (decreasing gradient).

Calculating Speed from a Distance-Time Graph — it's just the Gradient

For example, the speed of the return section of the graph is:

Speed = gradient = $\frac{vertical}{horizontal}$ = $\frac{500}{30}$ = 16.7 m/s

Don't forget that you have to use the scales of the axes to work out the gradient. Don't measure in cm!

Velocity-Time Graphs

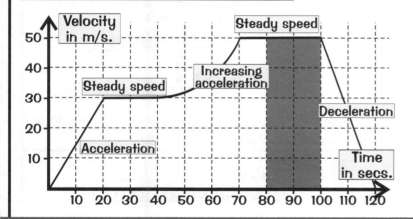

Very Important Notes:

1) Gradient = acceleration.
2) Flat sections represent steady speed.
3) The steeper the graph, the greater the acceleration or deceleration.
4) Uphill sections (/) show acceleration.
5) Downhill sections (\) show deceleration.
6) The area under any section of the graph (or all of it) is equal to the distance travelled in that time interval.
7) A curve means changing acceleration.

Calculating Acceleration, Speed and Distance from a Velocity-time Graph

1) The acceleration represented by the first section of the above velocity-time graph is:

Acceleration = gradient = $\frac{vertical}{horizontal}$ = $\frac{30}{20}$ = 1.5 m/s^2

2) The speed at any point is simply found by reading the value off the speed axis.
3) The distance travelled in any time interval is equal to the area. For example, the distance travelled between t=80 and t=100 is equal to the shaded area, which is equal to: 50 × 20 = 1000m.

Understanding speed and stuff — it can be an uphill struggle...

The tricky thing about these two kinds of graph is that they can look pretty much the same but represent totally different kinds of motion. If you want to be able to do them in the Exam then there's no substitute for simply learning all the numbered points for both types. Enjoy.

Force Diagrams

A <u>force</u> is simply a <u>push</u> or a <u>pull</u>. There are only <u>six different forces</u> for you to know about:

> 1) <u>GRAVITY</u> or <u>WEIGHT</u> — always acting <u>straight downwards</u>.
> 2) <u>REACTION FORCE</u> from a <u>surface</u>, usually acting <u>straight upwards</u>.
> 3) <u>THRUST</u> or <u>PUSH</u> or <u>PULL</u> due to an engine or rocket <u>speeding something up</u>.
> 4) <u>DRAG</u> or <u>AIR RESISTANCE</u> or <u>FRICTION</u> which is <u>slowing the thing down</u>.
> 5) <u>LIFT</u> due to an <u>aeroplane wing</u>.
> 6) <u>TENSION</u> in a <u>rope</u> or <u>cable</u>.

And there are basically only <u>FIVE DIFFERENT FORCE DIAGRAMS</u> you can get:

1) *Stationary Object* — All Forces in Balance

1) The force of <u>GRAVITY</u> (or <u>weight</u>) is acting <u>downwards</u>.

2) This causes a <u>REACTION FORCE</u> from the surface <u>pushing</u> the object <u>back up</u>.

3) This is the <u>only way</u> it can be in <u>BALANCE</u>.

4) <u>Without</u> a reaction force, it would <u>accelerate downwards</u> due to the pull of gravity.

5) The two <u>HORIZONTAL</u> forces must be <u>equal and opposite</u> otherwise the object will <u>accelerate sideways</u>.

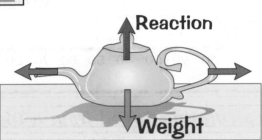

2) *Steady Horizontal Velocity* — All Forces in Balance!

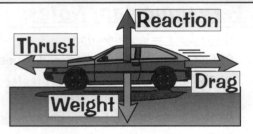

3) *Steady Vertical Velocity* — All Forces in Balance!

<u>TAKE NOTE</u>! To move with a <u>steady speed</u> the forces must be in <u>BALANCE</u>. If there's an <u>unbalanced force</u> then you get <u>ACCELERATION</u>, not steady speed. That's <u>rrrreally important</u> so don't forget it.

4) *Vertical Acceleration* — *Unbalanced Forces*

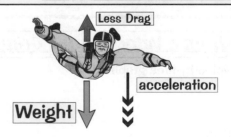

5) *Horizontal Acceleration* — *Unbalanced Forces*

The vertical forces are still <u>balanced</u> — so the only acceleration is in a horizontal direction.

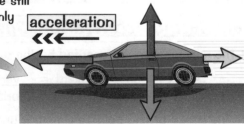

1) You only get <u>acceleration</u> with an overall <u>resultant</u> (unbalanced) <u>force</u>.
2) The <u>bigger</u> this <u>unbalanced force</u>, the <u>greater</u> the <u>acceleration</u>.

Revise Force Diagrams — but don't become unbalanced...

Make sure you learn those five different force diagrams. You'll almost certainly get one of them in your Exam. All you really need to remember is how the relative sizes of the arrows relate to the type of motion. It's pretty simple so long as you make the effort to <u>learn it</u>. So <u>scribble</u>...

Forces and Acceleration

Around about the time of the Great Plague in the 1660s, a chap called <u>Isaac Newton</u> worked out his <u>Laws of Motion</u>. At first they might seem kind of obscure or irrelevant, but to be perfectly blunt, if you can't understand these <u>simple laws</u> then you'll never fully understand <u>forces and motion</u>.

First Law — *Balanced Forces* **mean** *No Change* **in** *Velocity*

> **FIRST LAW:** So long as the forces on an object are all **BALANCED**, then it'll just **STAY STILL**, or else if it's already moving it'll just carry on at the **SAME VELOCITY**.

1) When a train or car or bus or anything else is <u>moving</u> at a <u>constant velocity</u> then the <u>forces</u> on it must all be <u>balanced</u>.
2) Never let yourself entertain the <u>ridiculous idea</u> that things need a constant overall force to <u>keep</u> them moving — NO NO NO NO NO NO!
3) To keep going at a <u>steady speed</u>, there must be <u>zero resultant force</u> — and don't you forget it.

Second Law — A *Resultant Force* **means** *Acceleration*

> **SECOND LAW:** If there is an **UNBALANCED FORCE**, then the object will **ACCELERATE** in that direction.

1) An <u>unbalanced</u> force will always produce <u>acceleration</u> (or deceleration).
2) This 'acceleration' can take the form of <u>starting</u>, <u>stopping</u>, <u>speeding up</u>, <u>slowing down</u> or <u>changing direction</u>. By changing <u>direction</u> you're changing <u>velocity</u> (ie. accelerating) without altering your speed.
3) On a force diagram, the <u>arrows</u> will be <u>unequal</u>.

Three Points **Which Should Be** Obvious:

1) The bigger the <u>force</u>, the <u>greater</u> the <u>acceleration</u> or <u>deceleration</u>.
2) The bigger the <u>mass</u>, the <u>smaller</u> the <u>acceleration</u>.
3) To get a <u>big</u> mass to accelerate <u>as fast</u> as a <u>small</u> mass it needs a <u>bigger</u> force. Just think about pushing <u>heavy</u> trolleys and it should all seem fairly <u>obvious</u>, I would hope.

The Overall Unbalanced Force *is called The* Resultant Force

Any <u>resultant force</u> will produce <u>acceleration</u> and this is the <u>formula</u> for it:

$$F = ma \qquad \text{or} \qquad a = F/m$$

m = mass, a = acceleration. F is always the <u>resultant force</u>.

<u>Example:</u> *What force is needed to accelerate a mass of 12kg at 5m/s² ?*
<u>Answer:</u> The question is asking for <u>force</u>.
Since they also give you values for <u>mass</u> and <u>acceleration</u>, the formula <u>F = ma</u> really should be a pretty <u>obvious</u> choice, surely.
So just <u>stick in</u> the numbers they give you where the letters are:
m = 12, a = 5, so "F = ma" gives F = 12 × 5 = <u>60N</u>   (It's Newtons because force always is.)

Notice that you don't really need to fully understand what's going on — you just need to know how to use formulae.)

It's no fun learning all this stuff — force yourself...

Good old Isaac. Those laws of motion are pretty inspirational don't you think? No? Oh. Well you could do with learning them anyway, because they'll be there <u>in the Exam</u>. Trust me.

Stopping Distances For Cars

They're pretty keen on this for Exam questions, so make sure you learn it properly.

The Many Factors Which Affect Your Total Stopping Distance

The distance it takes to stop a car is divided into the thinking distance and the braking distance.

1) Thinking Distance

"The distance the car travels in the split-second between a hazard appearing and the driver applying the brakes."

It's affected by three main factors:

a) **How FAST you're going** — obviously. Whatever your reaction time, the faster you're going, the further you'll go.

b) **How DOPEY you are** — This is affected by tiredness, drugs, alcohol, reaction time and a careless blasé attitude.

c) **How BAD the VISIBILITY is** — lashing rain and oncoming lights, etc. make hazards harder to spot.

The figures below for typical stopping distances are from the Highway code. It's frightening to see just how far it takes to stop when you're going at 70mph.

2) Braking Distance

"The distance the car travels during its deceleration whilst the brakes are being applied."

It's affected by four main factors:

a) **How FAST you're going** — obviously. The faster you're going, the further it takes to stop.

b) **How HEAVILY LOADED the vehicle is** — with the same brakes, a heavily-laden vehicle takes longer to stop. A car won't stop as quickly when it's full of people and luggage and towing a caravan.

c) **How good your BRAKES are** — all brakes must be checked and maintained regularly. Worn or faulty brakes will let you down catastrophically just when you need them the most, ie. in an emergency.

d) **How good the GRIP is** — this depends on three things:
1) road surface,   2) weather conditions,   3) tyres - including the condition of the tread and the tyre pressure.

30 mph	50 mph	70 mph
9m	15m	21m
14m	38m	75m
6 car lengths	13 car lengths	24 car lengths

Thinking distance

Braking distance

1) Leaves and diesel spills and muck on t'road are serious hazards because they're unexpected.

2) Wet or icy roads are always much more slippy than dry roads, but often you only discover this when you try to brake hard!

3) Tyres should have a minimum tread depth of 1.6mm. This is essential for getting rid of the water in wet conditions. Without tread, a tyre will simply ride on a layer of water and skid very easily. This is called "aquaplaning" and isn't nearly as cool as it sounds.

Muck on t'road, eh — by gum, it's grim up North...

They mention this specifically in the syllabus and are very likely to test you on it since it involves safety. Learn all the details and write yourself a mini-essay to see how much you really know.

Moments

When a force acts on something which has a <u>pivot</u>, it creates a 'turning force' called a <u>moment</u>.

What's a Turning Force Called? — Just a Moment...

A force that makes something <u>turn</u>, <u>twist</u> or <u>rotate</u> creates a <u>moment about a pivot</u>.

1) A '<u>moment</u>' is the '<u>turning effect</u>' produced by a force.

2) In screwdrivers, spanners etc, <u>linear forces</u> are <u>converted</u> into <u>turning forces</u> (<u>moments</u>).

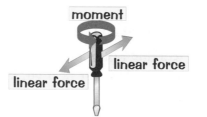 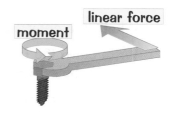

Calculating Moments — Just Use the Formula

MOMENT = FORCE × PERPENDICULAR DISTANCE

1) The units for <u>moments</u> are <u>newton-metres</u> (<u>Nm</u>).

2) This makes sense if you think about it, because you're multiplying a <u>force</u> (in N) by a <u>distance</u> (in m).

3) <u>Perpendicular distance</u> just means the distance to the pivot measured <u>at right angles to the line of the force</u>.

4) A moment can be <u>increased</u> by either <u>using more force</u>, or by <u>increasing the perpendicular distance</u> between the force and the pivot.

5) A door is much easier to open or close if you push at the <u>edge</u> of the door furthest from the hinge — you need <u>less force</u> to create the <u>same moment</u>.

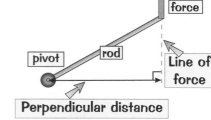

<u>Example</u>: *A force of 15N is applied at right angles to a plank of wood at a distance of 4m from the pivot. Find the moment about the pivot.*

15 N — Just multiply this force...
...by this distance. — 4 m — pivot

<u>Answer</u>: *Moment = Force × Perpendicular Distance*
*= 15 N × 4 m = **60Nm***

Equilibrium means Balanced Moments

1) For a system to be in <u>equilibrium</u>, (ie. all <u>nicely balanced</u> and <u>not moving</u>) then <u>this must be true</u>:

TOTAL <u>CLOCKWISE</u> MOMENT = TOTAL <u>ANTICLOCKWISE</u> MOMENT

2) Makes sense — if it had a <u>greater moment</u> in one direction than the other, it would <u>turn</u> in that direction.

<u>Example</u>: *Tantor the Elephant weighs 10,000N. He sits 0.5m from the pivot of a very long see-saw. (The see-saw's pivot is at its midpoint.) His friend Winston the mouse weighs just 2N. How far away from the pivot does Winston need to sit for the see-saw to be in equilibrium?*

<u>Answer</u>: *Clockwise moment due to Tantor = 10,000 N × 0.5 m = **5000Nm***
This must be equal to the anticlockwise moment.
Anticlockwise moment = 2 × d (= 5000 Nm)
*So d = **2500m*** *(It's a long see-saw.)*

2N — d — 0.5m — (Picture not to scale) — 10,000N

Let's twist again — like we did a moment ago...

This stuff isn't a whole lot of fun I know, but examiners can easily throw in a question about moments. <u>Practise</u> the examples so you know how it works, and <u>learn those formulae</u> real good.

Year 11 Exam　　Year 11 Exam　　Year 11 Exam　　Year 11 Exam　　Year 11 Exam　　Higher

Revision Summary for Module PD3

More jolly questions which I know you're going to really enjoy. There are lots of bits and bobs on forces and motion which you definitely need to know. Some bits are certainly quite tricky to understand, but there's also loads of straightforward stuff which just need to be learnt. You have to practise these questions over and over and over again, until you can answer them all really easily — phew, such fun.

1) What's the difference between speed and velocity? Give an example of each.

2) Write down the formula for working out speed. Find the speed of a partly chewed mouse which hobbles 3.2 m in 35 s. Find how far he'd get in 25 minutes at the same speed.

3) Describe how ticker-tape can be used to measure the speed of an object.

4) What's acceleration? Is it the same thing as speed or velocity? What are the units of it?

5) Write down the formula for acceleration.
What's the acceleration of a soggy pea, flicked from rest to a speed of 14 m/s in 0.4 s?

6) Sketch a typical distance-time graph and point out all the important parts of it.

7) Sketch a typical velocity-time graph and point out all the important parts of it.

8) Write down seven important points relating to each of these graphs.

9) Explain how to calculate velocity from a distance-time graph.

10) Explain how to find speed, distance and acceleration from a velocity-time graph.

11) List the six different kinds of forces you might find in a force diagram.
Sketch diagrams to illustrate them all.

12) Sketch each of the five standard force diagrams, showing the forces and the type of motion.

13) Write down the First Law of Motion. Illustrate with a diagram.

14) Write down the Second Law of Motion. Illustrate with a diagram. What's the formula for it?

15) A force of 30 N pushes on a trolley of mass 4 kg. What will be its acceleration?

16) What's the mass of a cat which accelerates at 9.8 m/s^2 when acted on by a force of 56 N?

17) What are the two different parts of the overall stopping distance of a car?

18) List the three or four factors which affect each of the two sections of stopping distance.

19) What is "aquaplaning"? How can you prevent it?.

20) Write down the formula for working out a moment. What are the units for a moment?

21) Give two ways of increasing a moment.

22) What's the condition for equilibrium, in terms of moments?

23) A narrow piece of wood rests on a pivot at its midpoint. A 3kg cat sits 50cm to the left of pivot. A 0.5kg mouse sits 135cm to the right of the pivot. Calculate the resultant moment. (Draw a diagram — it does help).

Answers

Index

Index

Index

Index